THE COMMUNITY INTERPRETER®

An International Workbook of Activities and Role Plays

for Medical, Educational and Social Services Interpreters

Marjory A. Bancroft, MA, Sofía García-Beyaert, MA, Katharine Allen, MA, Giovanna Carriero-Contreras, Denis Socarrás-Estrada, MA and Hank Dallmann, MA

Published by Culture & Language Press,
a division of Cross-Cultural Communications, LLC.

Culture & Language Press
10015 Old Columbia Road, Suite B-215
Columbia, MD 21046
410-312-5599

www.cultureandlanguage.net
clp@cultureandlanguage.net

Suggested citation

To refer to this workbook, please use the following format:
Bancroft, M.A., García-Beyaert, S., Allen, K., Carriero-Contreras, G., Socarrás-Estrada, D. &
Dallmann, H. (2015). *The Community Interpreter®: An International Workbook of Activities and
Role Plays*. (M. A. Bancroft, Ed.). Columbia, Maryland: Culture & Language Press.

Contents

INTRODUCTION

Purpose of the workbook

This workbook was created to support a textbook for the teaching of community interpreting. The workbook, like the textbook, is intended for use in universities, colleges and training programs in nearly any country where English is the language of instruction or where textbooks in English support education and training.

The program that this workbook supports was designed to train medical, educational and/or human services interpreters. Therefore, the activities and role plays include content in all three of these specializations to serve community interpreters who specialize in any or all of them.

How to use this workbook

In this workbook, all references to "the textbook" refer to *The Community Interpreter®: An International Textbook.*[1]

The chapters in this workbook are closely aligned with the five chapters of the textbook. The learning objectives, suggested activities and pedagogical approach also align with the textbook. While both the textbook and workbook can be used independently of each other, they will work best as companions.

Instructors and trainers of community interpreters will nonetheless find many valuable activities and role plays in this workbook that could be used to support nearly any program for teaching community interpreters, whether or not the textbook is also used. These activities and role plays can be individually selected as needed by instructors. However, the activities do follow a particular, intentional pedagogical pattern laid out in the textbook, which it closely follows.

In the United States, where the textbook and the workbook were created, this workbook supports university-based courses, including certificate programs, and also short training programs outside institutions of higher education. As a result, by intention the workbook contains far more exercises and role plays than could be used in a single course or in a short training program. The workbook could be used effectively to support courses of 40, 60 or 100 hours, or for longer programs. The number and variety of activities and role plays in the workbook allow it to be used in any way that an instructor thinks best.

Alternatively, the instructor teaching a single course or short program could assign activities and role plays in this workbook as home assignments, or for study and practice.

---

[1] Bancroft, M.A., García-Beyaert, S., Allen, K., Carriero-Contreras, G., and Socarrás-Estrada, D. (2015). *The Community Interpreter®: An International Textbook.* (M. A. Bancroft, Ed.). Columbia, Maryland: Culture & Language Press. See www. cultureandlanguage.net for more information or to order this and other books. There is also a website for the program: www. thecommunityinterpreter.com

Finally, this workbook—like its companion textbook—represents a valuable study resource, especially for interpreters who lack access to quality training programs and/or who are preparing for certification and other credentialing. Ideally, the interpreter will find another interpreter or two to work with, especially when practicing the role plays in this workbook. However, it will be difficult to obtain the fullest benefit from this workbook alone. Those who use this workbook for study will need to have access to the textbook to understand more fully how to execute the activities and role plays.

Teaching the "Medical Edition"

The organization that created this program, Cross-Cultural Communications, licenses trainers across the United States and in six other countries to teach the program, which is referred to as **The Community Interpreter® International Edition**. Many licensed trainers for the program choose to teach it as an "all medical" program, and that iteration is currently referred to as the Medical Edition. To accommodate such trainers and educators, and to make their work easier, *every activity or role play in this workbook that includes non-medical content* (i.e., content specific to non-healthcare settings, such as educational or social service settings) *is immediately followed by a comparable activity with exclusively medical content.*

Role plays

Most, but not all, role plays in this workbook include two versions in a convenient, easy-to-read table format: English only and English-Spanish (where Spanish is the language of the patient or client receiving the service).

The reason for including English-Spanish versions for most of the role plays is that a significant number of trainers who work with this program teach interpreters whose language pair is English-Spanish. Having role plays with English-Spanish texts allows for more realistic role playing. This format also makes the role plays easier to use in language-specific interpreter training programs for Spanish interpreters.

For all other languages, and for role plays that do not have a Spanish version, *students and training participants who share the same working languages and who play the patient, client or service user in role plays will sight translate the text into their other working language(s).* Doing so has two key benefits:
* The act of sight translating patient or service user dialogue provides sight translation practice for one role player who is not acting as the interpreter.
* Sight translation of the patient or client text permits the role plays to be used for any language combination.

Please note that in English-Spanish role plays, the Spanish version is not intended to be an exact translation but rather a rough equivalent of the English text for role play purposes only.

Instructor's guide

An instructor's guide exists for this program. This guide supports trainers and educators of interpreters by giving them clear instructions about how to deliver The Community Interpreter® International Edition in a 40- to 60-hour format. This instructor's guide is not currently for sale, although that situation might change in the future.

At the present time, the instructor's guide is available only for educators and trainers who attend a training-of-trainers (TOT) program delivered by Cross-Cultural Communications. This TOT has been delivered across the United States; a shorter version has been delivered elsewhere. If you would like to have this program brought to your institution or area, please send inquiries to clp@cultureandlanguage.net.

The instructor's guide contains answers to some, but not all, of the activities in this workbook and guidance for some, but not all, of the role plays. These answers and guidance are provided only for licensed trainers who plan to give 40- to 60-hour iterations of the program.

"Service user" vs. "client"

In writing a textbook that was intended for use in nearly any country in the world, the authors faced many interesting decisions regarding terms and concepts. The goal was always to be inclusive and write in a way that could be clearly understood across many societal contexts.

When referring to a consumer or provider of community services, the authors of the textbook made a conscious decision to adopt the terms "service user" and "service provider" respectively. (In the case of healthcare, the word "patient" seems to be the English term that is universally used.)

In the United States, however, the terms "client" and "provider" are widely used. Because this workbook will be used by many licensed trainers who are heavily concentrated in the United States, the term "client" has often been used in this workbook to replace "service user" in many activities. In addition, since so many licensed trainers for the program teach the Medical Edition, the term "patient/client" is also used in many of the activities.

Questions, comments and feedback

The authors are keenly interested in reader comments regarding the textbook and the workbook. Please do not hesitate to contact us in care of the publisher:

Culture & Language Press
+1-410-312-5599
clp@cultureandlanguage.net

LEARNING OBJECTIVES

After completing this chapter and its corresponding exercises, the learner will be able to:

OBJECTIVE 1.1

The Profession of Community Interpreting
Discuss the profession of community interpreting and four driving forces that have shaped the field.

OBJECTIVE 1.2

Interpreter Credentials
Analyze and compare interpreter credentials, including certificates and certification.

OBJECTIVE 1.3

Ethics and Standards for Community Interpreters
Demonstrate an understanding of eight core ethical principles for community interpreters.

OBJECTIVE 1.4

Application of Ethical Principles
Apply ethical principles for community interpreters to common communication barriers.

OBJECTIVE 1.5

Ethical Principles in Action
Examine two techniques for resolving ethical challenges in community interpreting.

OBJECTIVE 1.6

Reflective Practice
Explore the concept, meaning and application of "reflective practice" for community interpreters.

Learning Objective 1.1

After completing this section and its corresponding exercises, the learner will be able to:

- Discuss the profession of community interpreting and four driving forces that have shaped the field.

 Learning Activity 1.1(a): Defining Community and Medical Interpreting

Instructions

- Your instructor will divide you into groups of four.
- Each group will be given a large sheet of easel chart paper and a marker pen.
- As a group, come up with a definition for "interpreting" and "community interpreting." Think about what makes community interpreting different from other kinds of interpreting.
- Now define "medical" (or "healthcare") interpreting.
- Write your definitions onto the top portion of your easel chart paper.
- Attach your easel chart paper to the wall so that the rest of the group can see your definitions.
- Then, if you have any time remaining, in the lines provided answer the following questions:

1. Your definition of *interpreting* (in general)

_____

_____

_____

2. Your definition of *community* interpreting

_____

_____

_____

3. Your definition of *medical* interpreting

_____

_____

_____

4. List any common specializations of interpreting (e.g., medical interpreting, conference interpreting).

_____

_____

_____

_____

Learning Activity 1.1(b): The History of Community (and Medical) Interpreting

Instructions

- This activity is a lightning competition!
- In small groups, open your textbooks to pp. 44-49.
- Take a blank sheet of paper (per person or per group: your choice).
- Read and discuss the pages.
- You will have only 10-15 minutes to draw a timeline for *community or medical interpreting* (listen to your instructor's direction; otherwise it is your choice).
- Make your diagram in the form of a long arrow or arc with labels, like the one you see on p. 44 of your textbook.
- Your arrow or arc should be more detailed than the timeline on p. 44 (which is for *general* interpreting) and include *more information about the community and/or medical interpreting*.
- You may include information from friends, the Internet—even your smartphone.
- Now see which team comes up with the best timeline!

Learning Objective 1.2

After completing this section and its corresponding exercises, the learner will be able to:
- Analyze and compare interpreter credentials, including certificates and certification.

 Learning Activity 1.2: Interpreter Credentials and Certification

Instructions (Part A): Credentials

- Your instructor may choose to separate participants into two groups. One group will be called the "Term Group" and the other will be the "Definitions Group." (Note: for a smaller class, Terms could be posted on the walls.) Each "Definitions Group" could be divided into pairs or groups of three.
- When you are separated into Terms or Definitions groups, your instructor will ask you to close the workbook and give you a card that either has a term or a definition.
- The Term Group will stand in a straight line with space between each member. This group will stand still in place with each Term facing outward so that everyone can see what it says.
- Each member of the Definitions Group will try to find the correct term that fits the definition on his or her card.
- When everyone has found the right partner, each pair or group representative will read the Term and Definition out loud to the rest of the group.
- The correct answers are on the next page.

Terms and Definitions

Credential

A form of evidence or qualification that shows one's ability to carry out a certain job, task or type of work

Certification

A process by which a third party, whether a governmental, professional organization or accredited professional body, attests that an individual is qualified to provide a particular service (in other words, certification is an attestation that the individual has the capacity to perform a particular set of skills up to established benchmarks for professional performance[2])

Certificate

Official document attesting to a fact. For example, a training certificate could show proof of completion of a training program

Licensure

A credential that confers the legal authority to practice a profession

Portfolio assessment

Proof of credentials for languages or regions where interpreter skills tests may not be available

Training

Instruction that takes place outside an academic institution and which can range from a few hours to a few days or weeks

Education

Instruction that takes place inside an academic institution, ranging from a high school to post-graduate degree

Language proficiency certificate

A test to determine language proficiency (ideally performed using an externally validated test administered by qualified raters)

---

[2]Note however that on an international level certification can also be third-party attestation regarding the quality of products, systems or processes, not only persons, as defined in ISO 17000:2004: Conformity assessment – Vocabulary and general principles, definition 5.5.

Instructions (Part B): Interpreter qualifications and certification

Answer the following questions.
(**Note:** Medical interpreters will be directed to Part C, below)

1. Describe what you think are the *minimum* qualifications (such as educational level) that a community interpreter should possess.

_____

_____

_____

2. What minimum interpreting *skills* should a community interpreter master?

_____

_____

_____

3. Which broad categories of organizations develop professional interpreter certification that is accepted by the *profession* of interpreting as valid? Do not name any specific organizations. (For instance, if you think language companies create valid certification programs for interpreters, you could write "interpreting service providers.")

_____

_____

_____

4. Name any *specific* organizations you know that have developed certification for interpreters.

_____

_____

_____

Instructions (Part C): <u>Medical</u> interpreter qualifications and certification

Answer the following questions.

1. Describe what you think are the *minimum* qualifications (such as educational level) and skills (e.g., memory skills) that a medical interpreter should possess and state why.

_____

_____

_____

_____

2. Which broad categories of organizations develop professional medical interpreter certification that is accepted by the *profession* of medical interpreting as valid? Do not name any specific organizations. (For instance, if you think language companies create valid certification programs for interpreters, you could write "interpreting service providers.")

_____

_____

_____

3. Name any specific organizations you know that have developed certification for medical or healthcare interpreters.

_____

_____

_____

Instructions (Part D):Certification Role Plays

- These two role plays are both in English; you and your partner do not need to speak the same language.
- In pairs, simply assign each other one of the two roles and read the script out aloud.
- Then exchange roles and read each script aloud again.

1. The *Qualified* Interpreter: A Role Play

Number of participants: Two
Situation: Interview for a language company
Roles: The interpreter and an interviewer

Interviewer: Are you a certified interpreter?
Interpreter: No. In the U.S., except for the state of Washington, we have no certification for community interpreters, only for court and medical interpreters.
Interviewer: And you don't have one of those?
Interpreter: No.
Interviewer: So why should I hire you?
Interpreter: Well, I have a training certificate for professional community interpreter training, and two language proficiency certificates for my working languages, so I'm considered a *qualified interpreter*.

2. The *Certified* Interpreter: A Role Play

Number of participants: Two
Setting: Job interview for a hospital
Roles: Interpreter and human resources interviewer

Interviewer: Are you a certified interpreter?
Interpreter: Yes. I got certified by CCHI.
Interviewer: CCHI…
Interpreter: Certification Commission for Healthcare Interpreters. Here's my documentation.
Interviewer: Wait. Isn't there some other certification for medical?
Interpreter: Yes, NBCMI—the National Board of Certification for Medical Interpreters.
Interviewer: So which one is better?
Interpreter: The two are a bit different, but they're both valid. Here in the U.S., they're the only two national certification programs for medical interpreters.

Learning Objective 1.3

After completing this section and its corresponding exercises, the learner will be able to:
* Demonstrate an understanding of 9 core ethical principles for community interpreters.[3]

 Learning Activity 1.3(a): Communicative Autonomy: Role-Play Demonstration

Instructions

* The instructor will ask two class participants to volunteer for a role play to be demonstrated with the instructor in front of the entire class.
* Place three chairs in a semi-circle so that the class can observe those who participate in the role play.
* The group will play out five brief role play vignettes.
* The group will then answer these questions:

1. What is communicative autonomy? And why does it matter?

_____

_____

_____

_____

---

[3]Note that the textbook refers to 8 core ethical principles, not 9. However, this workbook, unlike the textbook, is focusing on a U.S.-based national code of ethics developed by the National Council on Interpreting in Health Care (*The National Code of Ethics for Interpreters in Health Care*, www.ncihc.org).

2. What is a code of ethics?

_____

_____

_____

3. What are standards of practice?

_____

_____

_____

4. What are some differences between ethics and standards of practice?

_____

_____

_____

5. How do ethics and standards for interpreters support communicative autonomy?

_____

_____

_____

DEMO ROLE PLAY SCRIPT #1

Doctor: You may have deep vein thrombosis, DVT, meaning a thrombus has formed in a deep vein in your right thigh, I suspect because you were stationary so long after surgery and your movements were confined.

Interpreter: You may have deep vein thrombosis, DVT, meaning a thrombus has formed in a deep vein in your right thigh, I suspect it's because you were stationary so long after surgery and your movements were confined.

Patient: Oh. (*looks confused*) Is this serious?

Interpreter: Oh, is this serious?

Doctor: It's potentially rather grave so I'll recommend an ultrasound. We'll be considering anticoagulants, and if they're contraindicated—in fact, glancing at your chart, I can see they might be—we might need to plan for an inferior vena cava filter.

Interpreter: Doctor, could you please simplify what you're saying? The patient comes from a small village in the countryside and she never graduated from elementary school. I'm not sure she's literate.
Interpreter: (*to patient*) I just clarified something with the doctor.

DEMO ROLE PLAY SCRIPT #2

Doctor: You may have deep vein thrombosis, DVT, meaning a thrombus has formed in a deep vein in your right thigh, I suspect because you were stationary so long after surgery and your movements were confined.

Interpreter: You may have deep vein thrombosis, DVT, in your right thigh, from a thrombus. A thrombus basically means a blood clot—something in your blood that stops you from bleeding. Maybe because you didn't move much after surgery.

DEMO ROLE PLAY SCRIPT #3

Doctor: You may have deep vein thrombosis, DVT, meaning a thrombus has formed in a deep vein in your right thigh, I suspect because you were stationary so long after surgery and your movements were confined.

Interpreter: You may have deep vein thrombosis, DVT, meaning a thrombus has formed in a deep vein in your right thigh, I suspect because you were stationary so long after surgery and your movements were confined.

Patient: Oh. (*looks confused*) Is this serious?

Interpreter: Oh, is this serious? (*to doctor*) Doctor, the interpreter is concerned that what I interpreted about DVT isn't clear. Maybe if you explain what DVT is, I can interpret this more clearly.

Interpreter: (*to patient*) The interpreter just clarified with the doctor that I'm concerned what I interpreted about DVT might not be clear. I suggested perhaps if he explains what DVT is, I could interpret this more clearly.

DEMO ROLE PLAY SCRIPT #4

Client/Patient: (*to the provider*) You suck. I can't stand what you're doing to me. Fuck you.

Interpreter: (*to the provider*) S/he said some bad words—s/he's angry.

DEMO ROLE PLAY SCRIPT #5

Client/Patient: (*to the provider*) You suck. I can't stand what you're doing to me. Fuck you.

Interpreter: (*to the provider*) You suck. I can't stand what you're doing to me. Fuck you.

Note to the interpreter: "Fuck you" has many possible ways of being expressed in another language. Use any offensive, colloquial expression that respects the language register and meaning. Do <u>not</u> soften the language.

Instructions

- In pairs, practice saying out loud The Community Interpreter's Pledge from the textbook (p. 8), and reproduced below, or the Medical Interpreter's pledge (below), which matches the nine principles of the *National Code of Ethics for Interpreters in Health Care*. Recite the pledge you choose in both or all your working languages by sight translating the pledge after reciting it in English.
- Now discuss with your partner:
    - What did you like about this pledge?
    - What did not seem clear to you?
    - Did anything in the pledge surprise or disturb you?

THE COMMUNITY INTERPRETER'S PLEDGE

As a community interpreter, I will support the communicative autonomy of the parties I interpret for. To help them maintain responsibility for and control over their own communication, I will:

Observe confidentiality.

Strive for accuracy.

Display impartiality.

Ensure transparency.

Promote direct communication.

Respect professional boundaries.

Support intercultural communication.

Maintain professional conduct.

THE MEDICAL INTERPRETER'S PLEDGE

As a medical interpreter, I will support the communicative autonomy of the parties I interpret for. To help them maintain responsibility for and control over their own communication, I will:

Observe confidentiality.

Strive for accuracy.

Display impartiality.

Respect professional boundaries.

Develop cultural awareness.

Treat all parties with respect.

Consider careful advocacy.

Further my knowledge and skills.

Maintain professional conduct.

Note: This version of the pledge is based on the NCIHC *National Code of Ethics for Interpreters in Health Care.*

Instructions

- Working in pairs, match the correct ethical principle to its corresponding definition.
- The team that finishes first and is correct wins this competitive activity.
- Community interpreters can choose Part A: Textbook principles.
- Medical interpreters can choose Part B: NCIHC principles.

Part A: Textbook principles

Ethical Topic	Principle Letter	Ethical Principle
1. Confidentiality		a. The community interpreter refrains from allowing personal beliefs to manifest in his or her professional conduct, especially when rendering the content and tone of the message.
2. Accuracy		b. The community interpreter initiates and actively supports practices that enable the service users and providers to engage in direct communication.
3. Impartiality		c. The community interpreter intervenes to promote meaningful communication across cultural differences only when necessary for clear communication and without articulating the interpreter's beliefs or speculations about any of the parties' cultures.
4. Transparency		d. The community interpreter should maintain professional boundaries, both during and outside the interpreted encounter.
5. Direct Communication		e. The community interpreter's conduct should reflect the highest standards of the profession by showing adherence to professional ethics and best practices.
6. Professional Boundaries		f. The community interpreter does not disclose private or proprietary information learned during the execution of his or her professional duties, except where disclosure is required by institutional regulations or by law.
7. Intercultural Communication		g. The community interpreter interprets everything that is said to ensure that all messages expressed during the encounter are communicated to all parties.
8. Professional Conduct		h. The community interpreter strives to interpret every message without omissions, additions, distortions or any other changes to the original message.

Part B: NCIHC principles

Excerpted from NCIHC (2004): National Code of Ethics for Interpreters in Health Care.

Ethical Topic	Principle Letter	Ethical Principle
1. Confidentiality		a. The interpreter strives to maintain impartiality and refrains from counseling, advising or projecting personal biases or beliefs.
2. Accuracy		b. When the patient's health, well-being, or dignity is at risk, the interpreter may be justified in acting as an advocate. Advocacy is understood as an action taken on behalf of an individual that goes beyond facilitating communication, with the intention of supporting good health outcomes. Advocacy must only be undertaken after careful and thoughtful analysis of the situation and if other less intrusive actions have not resolved the problem.
3. Impartiality		c. The interpreter continuously strives to develop awareness of his/her own and other (including biomedical) cultures encountered in the performance of their professional duties.
4. Role boundaries		d. The interpreter maintains the boundaries of the professional role, refraining from personal involvement.
5. Cultural awareness		e. The interpreter must at all times act in a professional and ethical manner.
6. Respect		f. The interpreter treats as confidential, within the treating team, all information learned in the performance of their professional duties, while observing relevant requirements regarding disclosure.
7. Advocacy		g. The interpreter strives to render the message accurately, conveying the content and spirit of the original message, taking into consideration its cultural context.
8. Professional Development		h. The interpreter strives to continually further his/her knowledge and skills.
9. Professionalism		i. The interpreter treats all parties with respect.

Learning Objective 1.4

After completing this section and its corresponding exercises, the learner will be able to:
- Apply ethical principles for community interpreters to common communication barriers.

 Learning Activity 1.4(a): Ethical Principles: Application

Instructions

- Working in groups of two or three, read the following scenarios in Section I and/or Sections II and III as your instructor advises.
- Answer the questions that follow each scenario.

Section I: Common ethical challenges in community interpreting

1. The client or patient is so grateful for your interpreting that she wants to give you a small bracelet as a gift. What should you do? Which ethical principles apply to this situation?

_____

_____

_____

2. You arrive at the assignment and find out that the patient/client is your second cousin. You barely know him. What should you do? Which ethical principles apply to this situation?

_____

_____

_____

3. The doctor asks if the patient can come back in three weeks. Instead of answering this question, the patient or service user talks for three minutes about family matters. What should you do? Will you interpret everything? Which ethical principles apply to this situation?

_____

_____

_____

4. You wear a T-shirt and sandals for an assignment at a mobile health clinic or small nonprofit agency in a rural area where healthcare and service providers dress casually. Is this dress acceptable? Why or why not? Which ethical principles apply to this situation?

_____

_____

_____

5. The patient/client has many problems that worry you deeply. She is a refugee, and you are a refugee from the same country. She asks for your personal telephone number. What should you do? Which ethical principles apply to this situation?

_____

_____

_____

6. A patient/client is experiencing domestic violence. She shares this information with you privately but asks you not to tell anyone. You are afraid she will be seriously hurt. May you tell a colleague about her situation? Why or why not? Which ethical principles apply to this situation?

_____

_____

_____

7. You have very strong feelings about childhood sexual abuse. You are asked to interpret in therapy for a pedophile (someone who sexually abuses children). Will you accept the assignment? Why or why not? Which ethical principles apply to this situation?

_____

_____

_____

8. You interpret for a child who has bruises. In the parents' culture, as you are aware, strong physical discipline is often encouraged. But you see the hospital social worker is probably going to report the parent for child abuse. Should you raise the cultural issue? Why or why not? Which ethical principles apply to this situation?

_____

_____

_____

9. You interpret at a school health room for a child who has red marks that come from a common healing remedy in the parents' culture. The health aide is clearly unaware of the practice. You know of several cases where parents were arrested for this practice, though their intention is to heal the child. Should you mention the cultural remedy? Why or why not? Which ethical principles apply to this situation?

_____

_____

_____

10. A patient tells you that he has HIV. But then he adds, "Don't tell the doctor. He might tell my wife!" May you share this information with the doctor? Why or why not? Which ethical principles apply to this situation?

_____

_____

_____

Section II: Advanced ethical challenges for general community interpreters

Ethical Challenge 1: A Punjabi-speaking father has been summoned to a disciplinary proceeding for his son, who is facing expulsion from a school. Sometimes the father jumps in to answer questions directly in English, cutting off the interpreter. Other times, he begins to answer in the language of the school, then gets stuck and looks to the interpreter for help. Sometimes it is clear to the interpreter from the answers that the father gives that he hasn't fully understood what has been said.

What should the interpreter do?

_____

_____

_____

Which ethical principles apply to this situation?

_____

_____

Ethical Challenge 2: You are interpreting for a social worker taking a case history for a service user seeking shelter and food aid. The social worker consistently turns to you and says "Can you ask her how many children she has?" or "Please tell her that our services are limited to a month's stay." The service user is speaking directly to you and not the social worker.

What should the interpreter do?

_____

_____

_____

Which ethical principles apply to this situation?

_____

_____

Ethical Challenge 3: The mother repeatedly nods her head in apparent understanding as the school psychologist discusses the results of her son's developmental evaluation, but it's rather clear to the interpreter from the mother's body language and tone of voice that she does not agree with the recommended services. However, the psychologist is not noticing these nonverbal communication cues.

What should the interpreter do?

_____

_____

_____

Which ethical principles apply to this situation?

_____

_____

Ethical Challenge 4: You are interpreting for a school counselor who is meeting with the parents of a middle-school girl who has suddenly dropped out of all extracurricular activities. The counselor urges the parents to give the girl permission to continue on the track team and after-school homework club. The parents are vague in their answers and uncooperative. You suspect that the girl is being asked to babysit younger siblings after school, a common practice for this culture. The counselor turns to you and says, "What's wrong with these parents? Do they think girls aren't good enough to play sports? They're really messing up their daughter."

What should the interpreter do?

_____

_____

_____

Which ethical principles apply to this situation?

_____

_____

Ethical Challenge 5: The patient is an indigenous woman from Guatemala who does not speak Spanish well. The hospital has limited access to interpreters who speak her native language, Quiche. She is in the intensive care unit because of a serious ulcer that could require surgery. She is undergoing multiple tests that require her to fast, with no food or water allowed.

The patient is convinced that her illness is being caused by the fasting and is trying to leave. The Quiche interpreter is unavailable so you, the Spanish-speaking interpreter, are called in to convince the patient to stay and receive the tests.

What should the interpreter do?

_____

_____

_____

Which ethical principles apply to this situation?

_____

_____

Ethical Challenge 6: You've been assigned to interpret at a local housing services agency for several clients during the course of a few weeks. The offices have an open setup with multiple desks and little privacy. As a result, you clearly see that the service users you are interpreting for are not being offered some of the same services available to other clients who speak the language of service. You suspect discrimination.

What should the interpreter do?

_____

_____

_____

Which ethical principles apply to this situation?

_____

_____

Section III: Advanced ethical challenges for medical interpreters

Ethical Challenge 1: A Punjabi-speaking father is speaking with the anesthesiologist who needs to obtain a consent for surgery. Sometimes the father jumps in to answer questions directly in English, cutting off the interpreter. Other times, he'll begin to answer in the language of the hospital, then get stuck and look to the interpreter for help. Sometimes it is clear to the interpreter from the answers the father gives that he hasn't fully understood what has been said.

What should the interpreter do?

_____

_____

_____

Which ethical principles apply to this situation?

_____

_____

Ethical Challenge 2: You are interpreting for the hospital social worker for a patient who needs to be transferred to a medical rehabilitation center. The social worker consistently turns to you and says, "Can you ask her if she has her insurance card with her?" or "Please tell her that Medicare will only cover a month's stay and she needs to be there for six weeks." The patient is directing her comments directly to you in response to the social worker's questions.

What should the interpreter do?

_____

_____

_____

Which ethical principles apply to this situation?

_____

_____

Ethical Challenge 3: The mother repeatedly nods her head in apparent understanding as the neuropsychologist discusses the results of her son's developmental evaluation (after the son suffered a serious head injury), but it's rather clear to the interpreter from the mother's body language and tone of voice that she does not agree with the recommended services. However, the psychologist is not noticing these nonverbal communication cues.

What should the interpreter do?

_____

_____

_____

Which ethical principles apply to this situation?

_____

_____

Ethical Challenge 4: You are interpreting for a physical therapist who is meeting with the parents of a 13 year-old girl who is consistently missing her twice-weekly appointments to treat a shoulder injury. The physical therapist is urging the parents to make sure the girl continues her physical therapy. The parents are vague in their answers and insist that their daughter's shoulder is fine. You suspect that the girl is needed to babysit younger siblings after school, a common practice for this culture. The physical therapist turns to you and says, "What is wrong with these parents? Don't they realize that this shoulder injury could become permanent if she doesn't fully rehabilitate it? They are really messing up their daughter."

What should the interpreter do?

_____

_____

_____

Which ethical principles apply to this situation?

_____

_____

Ethical Challenge 5: The patient is an indigenous woman from Guatemala who does not speak Spanish well. The hospital has limited access to interpreters who speak her native language, Quiche. She is in the intensive care unit because of a serious ulcer that could require surgery. She is undergoing multiple tests that require her to fast, with no food or water allowed.

The patient is convinced that her illness is being caused by the fasting and is trying to leave. The Quiche interpreter is unavailable so you, the Spanish-speaking interpreter, are called in to convince the patient to stay and receive the tests.

What should the interpreter do?

_____

_____

_____

Which ethical principles apply to this situation?

_____

_____

 Learning Activity 1.4(b): Ethical Principles: "Yes, No, Maybe"

Note: This activity focuses on four ethical principles: confidentiality, accuracy, impartiality and professional boundaries.

Instructions

- In pairs or small groups, write an answer (yes, no or maybe) for each scenario below in either Section I (general community interpreting) *or* Section II (medical interpreting).
- **Medical interpreters please select Section II.**
- For the large group discussion, use your green (YES), red (NO) laminated cards to answer the instructor for each question.
- Hold up your green card for ethical scenarios to indicate that you agree with the interpreter's choice, hold up your red card for if you disagree, and hold up both cards if you are unsure or feel there is no easy answer.
- State which ethical principles apply for each scenario.

Ethical Scenarios, Section I: General community interpreting

Yes	Ethical Scenario	Ethical Principles
Yes No Maybe	1. When the service provider pulls the interpreter aside after the session and asks, "I'm worried about this client, can you tell me what you think is really going on?" the interpreter shares with the provider what she knows about the client from her contact with the client in the community.	
Yes No Maybe	2. When the service provider leaves, the service user leans in to the interpreter and says, "I missed my appointment last week because my husband hit me and my face was bruised. But don't tell the case worker, she might take my kids away." The interpreter chooses to honor the service user's request and doesn't share this information with the service provider.	
Yes No Maybe	3. The local high school sponsored a community workshop on bullying prevention for which you interpreted. At the meeting, the father of one student shared that his son had been bullied so badly by his fellow classmates that he tried to kill himself and spent time in a psychiatric residential program as a result. The following week, you are with a group of friends who discuss this family's troubles and you share what you heard at the public event.	
Yes No Maybe	4. You have just completed an interpreting assignment for a workers' compensation[4] medical exam. You phone the interpreting agency to give a report. The agency rep says: "Okay, now I need you to give me a summary of the decisions made during the exam. Did the patient qualify for additional medical services?" You do your best to give an accurate summary.	
Yes No Maybe	5. During an interview with a social worker, the service user gets frustrated and starts cursing and calls the social worker "racist." You interpret the offensive language exactly as the service user says it.	
Yes No Maybe	6. You are interpreting for a family whose daughter has developmental delays. The psychologist who tested the daughter is reporting the results of the exam, which will determine whether the child receives services. It is clear to you, the interpreter, that the family members do not understand what the psychologist is saying because she uses complicated language, so you do your best to simplify the language without changing its meaning.	

---

[4]Workers' compensation programs provide health and rehabilitation services for workers injured on the job. Such programs exist in many countries around the world.

Yes No Maybe	7. You are interpreting for a service provider and a client. The provider is trying to get yes or no responses from her client, but the client answers every question with a long, rambling story. The provider is getting annoyed. You instruct the client to stop telling the story and only answer yes or no.	
Yes No Maybe	8. During an assignment at a refugee resettlement agency, you are asked to sight translate a complicated legal form, one you have never seen before. You have had no formal training in legal terminology, and you don't often sight translate. When you express your doubts about your competence, the refugee agency worker begs you to do the sight translation because no other interpreter is available. You reluctantly agree and sight translate the document.	
Yes No Maybe	9. During an interview with an immigration official to obtain asylum, the woman becomes distraught and starts to cry and shake when she describes the threats that caused her to leave her homeland. She is terrified she won't get legal status to stay in the new country. The immigration official ignores the woman's distress and continues with the interview. You feel uncomfortable for not providing her with any kind of comfort, so you take her hand and offer her a tissue to wipe her tears.	
Yes No Maybe	10. Walking into a school disciplinary hearing, you realize the parents and their daughter are your neighbors. However, qualified interpreters for your language pair are hard to find. You feel you have a good relationship with your neighbors so you stay to interpret and don't inform the service provider that you know the service users.	
Yes No Maybe	11. During an interpreting assignment, a woman whose housing subsidy is being terminated starts to yell loudly at the housing official. She shakes her fist in anger. You know that as the interpreter you are supposed to faithfully capture her tone and emotion, so you also raise your voice and shake your fist.	
Yes No Maybe	12. After a lawyer-client interview, the lawyer asks you, "So talk to me about the relationships between men and women in your culture. Do men always tell the women what to do?" You try to explain how your culture expects women and men to interact.	
Yes No Maybe	13. Saira has just finished interpreting for her paid assignment for a new arrival at her local family violence program.[5] Just as the session ends, the agency director asks the interpreter to accompany the service user to the shelter and to stay there while the woman "settles in." Saira refuses because she doesn't feel comfortable driving the client in her car.	

[5] The terms used most often in many countries are "intimate partner violence" and "gender-based violence," terms that include sexual violence. In other countries, such as the United States and Canada, the terms "domestic violence" (abuse by an intimate partner, although definitions vary) or "sexual assault" are used. "Family violence" is another term used: it can refer to domestic violence, child abuse and/or incest, among other crimes.

Ethical Scenarios, Section II: Medical interpreting

Yes	Ethical Scenario	Ethical Principle
Yes No Maybe	1. The nurse pulls the interpreter aside after the session and asks "I'm worried about this patient, can you tell me what you think is really going on?" The interpreter shares with the provider what she knows about the client from her contact with her in the community.	
Yes No Maybe	2. When the doctor leaves, the patient leans in to the interpreter and says "I missed my appointment last week because my husband hit me and my face was bruised. But don't tell the doctor, I'm afraid she'll report my husband and my kids will get taken away." The interpreter chooses to honor the patient's request and doesn't share this information with the doctor.	
Yes No Maybe	3. The local clinic sponsored a health fair that had a public presentation on how to prevent sexually transmitted infections. At the presentation, a man stood up and shared that his son had gotten HIV from sharing needles when using drugs. His son tried to kill himself and had to spend time in a rehabilitation program. The following week, you are with a group of friends who discuss this family's troubles and you share what you heard at the public event.	
Yes No Maybe	4. You have just completed an interpreting assignment for a workers' compensation[6] medical exam. You phone the interpreting agency to give a report. The agency rep says: "Okay, now I need you to give me a summary of the decisions made during the exam. Did the patient qualify for additional medical services?" You do your best to give an accurate summary.	
Yes No Maybe	5. During an interview with the hospital social worker, the patient gets frustrated and starts cursing and calls the social worker "racist." You interpret the offensive language exactly as the patient says it.	
Yes No Maybe	6. You are interpreting for a family whose daughter has developmental delays. The psychologist who tested the daughter is reporting the results of the exam, which will determine whether the child will be eligible for speech and physical therapy services. It is clear to you, the interpreter, that the family members do not understand what the psychologist is saying because she uses complicated language, so you do your best to simplify the language without changing its meaning.	

---

[6]Workers' compensation programs provide health and rehabilitation services for workers injured on the job. Such programs exist in many countries around the world.

Yes No Maybe	7. You are interpreting for a patient and hospital admissions worker. The admissions worker is trying to get yes or no responses from the patient to fill out the paperwork, but the patient answers every question trying to explain in great detail what is wrong with her. The admissions worker is getting annoyed. You instruct the patient to stop telling the story and only answer yes or no.	
Yes No Maybe	8. During an assignment at a clinic for a patient who is participating in a drug research trial, you are asked to sight translate a complicated legal form, one you have never seen before. You have had no formal training in legal terminology, and you don't often sight translate. When you express your doubts about your competence, the clinic coordinator begs you to do the sight translation because no other interpreter is available. You reluctantly agree and sight translate the document.	
Yes No Maybe	9. During a gynecological exam, the woman becomes distraught and starts to cry and shake when the doctor is ready to do the vaginal exam. The patient is clearly terrified and moans loudly during the procedure. The doctor ignores the woman's distress and continues with the exam. You feel uncomfortable for not providing her with any kind of comfort, so you take her hand and offer her a tissue to wipe her tears.	
Yes No Maybe	10. Walking into an appointment with a visiting oncologist, you realize the patient is your daughter's teacher. However, qualified interpreters for your language pair are hard to find. You feel you have a good relationship with your daughter's teacher so you don't say anything about it and stay to interpret.	
Yes No Maybe	11. During an interpreting assignment, a woman who is told that her baby's fever and flu symptoms will get better without taking antibiotics begins to yell loudly at the doctor. She shakes her fist in anger. You know that as the interpreter you are supposed to faithfully capture her tone and emotion, so you also raise your voice and shake your fist.	
Yes No Maybe	12. After a patient-doctor visit where a husband and wife were present, the doctor asks you, "So talk to me about the relationships between men and women in your culture. Do men always tell the women what to do?" You try to explain how your culture expects women and men to interact.	
Yes No Maybe	13. Saira has just finished interpreting for her paid assignment for a new arrival at psychiatric unit. Just as the session ends, the agency director asks the interpreter to accompany the patient to the residential area, which is located several buildings away, and to stay there while the woman "settles in." Sara refuses because she doesn't feel comfortable being alone with the patient during such a long walk.	

Learning Objective 1.5

After completing this section and its corresponding exercises, the learner will be able to:
- Practice two techniques for resolving ethical challenges in community interpreting.

 Learning Activity 1.5(a): Decision-making Protocols and Practice: The CHIA Tool

Instructions

- In groups of two or three, apply the CHIA Ethical Decision-making Process to the following scenario.
- Go through the tool step by step, imagining what the interpreter could do for each of the six steps.

Scenario

You regularly interpret for a family with a young child receiving early intervention services for developmental delays (in other words, the child is not developing "on schedule" and needs professional help). The family is also receiving food assistance, including vouchers to buy formula for the child. When the child turns one, the program stops providing formula and provides vouchers for milk only.

At the next evaluation, after the child turns one, the mother is concerned about a new rash that has developed on the baby's hands and feet. You have seen that kind of rash before and are sure it is caused by a milk allergy, which is not rare. You also know that food allergies can aggravate some kinds of developmental delays. Yet the providers don't seem concerned. The mother, increasingly frustrated at their lack of attention to the rash, turns to you to ask for advice.

What should you do?

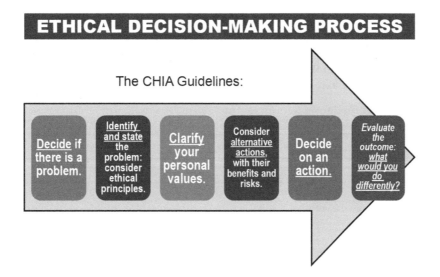

ETHICAL DECISION-MAKING PROCESS

The CHIA Guidelines:

Decide if there is a problem. | Identify and state the problem: consider ethical principles. | Clarify your personal values. | Consider alternative actions, with their benefits and risks. | Decide on an action. | Evaluate the outcome: what would you do differently?

1. <u>Ask questions to determine whether there is a problem.</u>
Assume you can ask the questions in your own mind: you don't need to ask questions out loud. Why is this situation a problem? What are some possible consequences if you do not speak up and simply interpret?

_____

_____

_____

2. <u>Identify and clearly state the problem, considering the ethical principles that may apply and ranking them in applicability.</u>
What is the problem here? Which ethical principles might apply to this situation? Which ethical principles are the <u>most important</u> in this situation (in your opinion)?

_____

_____

_____

3. <u>Clarify personal values as they relate to the problem.</u>
Discuss your own personal values in this situation. For example, perhaps you feel you should be loyal and helpful to people from your own country, or that patients have a right to an in-person interpreter when they hear difficult and painful news.

_____

_____

_____

4. <u>Consider alternative actions, including benefits and risks.</u>
Write down <u>three different things</u> you could do to address this situation (even if one of them is simply to interpret and take no action); then discuss the advantages and disadvantages of each option.

_____

_____

_____

5. <u>Decide to carry out the action chosen.</u>
From the three options you just wrote down, select the action you think you would carry out in real life in this situation.

_____

_____

_____

6. <u>Evaluate the outcome and consider what might be done differently next time.</u>
Since you did not encounter this situation in real life, try to imagine one or two of the possible consequences (one positive, one negative) and how you would feel about them.

_____

_____

_____

 Learning Activity 1.5(b): The SAY NO Model

Instructions

- The instructor will post the **SAY NO** Model in a place clearly visible to all participants. The steps of this model are:
    - √ Be gracious.
    - √ Offer choices.
    - √ Give reasons.
- The instructor will distribute to each participant a slip with an inappropriate request often made to community interpreters and medical interpreters—see below. The class participants will stand and form a large circle, big enough to include everyone.
- Using a light ball or other light object, each participant will take turns tossing the ball to a classmate and read out the content of his or her slip. The person who catches the ball will practice saying "no" following the **SAY NO** model. The group may offer assistance.
- If time permits, your instructor will choose three examples from the lists below or the ones given after the scenarios: write out in the lines provided what you would say to practice the SAY NO model.

Inappropriate requests made to community interpreters (general examples)

Provider
- Stay here and help the patient/client fill out the form. I'll be right back.
- I need this document translated by tomorrow. (The interpreter is not qualified to translate.)
- Please talk to me about the religious issues—I don't understand what was going on in there.
- Receptionist: Mrs. Nguyen is so sweet! How did her appointment go?
- Please sight translate this consent form while I run down the hall.
- Could you transport the patient down the hall? You just push. (*hospital setting*)
- Okay, now go over the medication instructions with her to be sure she understands.

Service user/patient
- What do you think—should I stay with this provider?
- Please accept this gift—it's nothing, really!
- Could you just give me your telephone number? My family is having so many problems, and we just got to this country!
- Please tell me if my husband is okay after his surgery! I know you were just interpreting for him.

- Could you tell me what this letter says? I think it's from the gas company.
- Is my child going to die?
- I need a lift home. I think you live in that direction—couldn't you take me? It's snowing, and you know I'm pregnant.
- Tell the doctor about the fasting. You know how it works. Maybe it's important for the medication.

Other SAY NO scenarios

Non-Medical

Scenario A: You have interpreted for a father with a school secretary, teacher and now the principal. When the principal asks the father to tell her what the student's problems are, the father says to you, the interpreter: "You know what my problems are. Can you tell the principal about them? I don't want to have to say them again."

Scenario B: After an appointment with the housing services worker, the service user is grateful and wants to pay you for your help. "Thank you so much for helping me today. Here is a little something. It's not much money, but I really want to give it to you."

Scenario C: You have just entered the classroom with the father, child and teacher. The teacher turns to you and says: "You know all the questions I ask at the beginning—in fact, you must know them in your sleep by now. Can you ask him those questions while I go and get the student's records, which I forgot? I'll be right back."

Medical

Scenario D: The patient is in a wheelchair and needs to go from his room to radiology for X-rays. The nurse is busy and needs to see another patient. She says to you: "Can you push Mr. Garcia in his wheelchair down the hall to radiology? I really need to see another patient."

Scenario E: A patient has just met with the surgeon who has explained the knee surgery the patient will have the next day. The surgeon turns to you and says: "All that's left is for the patient to sign this consent form. Can you explain it to him and then have him sign it?"

Scenario F: The speech therapist needs the student's mother to practice the exercises she will have to do with her son at home. But the mother has brought her other child, a baby with her. The baby is fussing and distracting the mother. The speech therapist says to you, "Can you hold the baby for a few minutes while I teach the mother how to do these exercises?"

How will *you* SAY NO?

Example 1

Provider: Could you please explain this form to him while I check in with the next patient?

_____

_____

_____

_____

Example 2

Patient/Client: This gift is very small, but I really wanted to show my appreciation!

_____

_____

_____

_____

Example 3

Provider: Please translate this by next week, it's a really important document. (Note: This example is about translation, not sight translation. For purposes of this exercise, you are not qualified to translate.)

_____

_____

_____

_____

Learning Objective 1.6

After completing this section and its corresponding exercises, the learner will be able to:
- Explore the concept, meaning and application of "reflective practice" for community interpreters.

 Learning Activity 1.6(a): Reflective Practice: A Role Play Demonstration

Instructions

- The instructor will recruit three class participants to help with a role-play demonstration in front of the class using one of the role plays below. Using the role play chosen, the participants will play a service provider, patient or service user and interpreter (who will go from English to English). The instructor will pull the interpreter aside and tell the interpreter to do a poor job while interpreting.
- During the role play, the instructor will help the interpreter, give advice and keep interrupting. When the role play is finished, the instructor will give the participant who played the interpreter negative feedback in a very unconstructive way. Then the instructor will ask the class to comment on how s/he provided feedback to the interpreter. Was the feedback effective? How might the interpreter feel?
- Next, the instructor will give overly positive feedback to the interpreter, saying everything was wonderful and how brilliant the interpreter was. Participants will then be asked to comment on how well the positive feedback worked or didn't work.
- The group will then repeat part of the demonstration role play in front of the class and this time the interpreter is not interrupted at all, even when s/he struggles or has difficulties. When the role play is done, the instructor provides feedback following the guidelines for providing feedback offered below.

Guideline for providing reflective practice feedback:

- *Always let the interpreter speak first: let the <u>interpreter</u> report what <u>he or she</u> thought went well or what mistakes were made before you give feedback!*
- *Make **positive comments first**.*
- *Be specific about where errors were made or improvements are possible.*
- *Be as neutral as possible when noting errors.*
- *Be humble.*
- *Provide solutions for the interpreter.*
- *Point out repetitive errors.*
- *Don't overwhelm the interpreter by providing too much feedback—or providing too little.*
- *Observe and be sensitive to the interpreter's response to your feedback.*

Learning Activity 1.6(b): Reflective Practice: A Partner Learning Exercise

Instructions

(Note: This activity can be done in pairs or with the instructor leading the entire group).

- Turn on your recording device and make sure it is working. Put on your headset or ear buds.
- Start recording when the role play reading begins.
- Your partner will read both parts of role play provided. Ideally, you will be in same-language pairs. If that is the case, your partner will read one part in English and sight translate the other part in your shared non-English language.
- You will *not* look at the role play text when it is your turn to interpret.
- Interpret the role play consecutively, recording yourself.
- When you play the interpreter or read the role play script out loud, ___DO NOT interrupt the interpreting for any reason___. Stay in your role and either keep interpreting even if you make a mistake (if you are the interpreter), or keep reading the role play script. ___Do NOT help the interpreter while s/he is interpreting___. Allow the *interpreter* to solve problems alone.
- When the role play is finished, stop interpreting and turn off your recording device.
- If working in pairs, switch roles so that both of you have a chance to play the interpreter. Your partner will follow the same instructions.
- Taking turns, listen back to your interpreting on the recording device. Follow along with the written role play. Note what you did well first. Also note any errors or areas to improve.
- Tell each other at least one area that you have identified that you want to work on in your consecutive interpreting.
- If both of you have finished one role play each, select another role play and continue.
- Switch roles so that both of you have a chance to play the interpreter. Your partner will follow steps 1-5 of the bullet points above.

Interpreting Feedback Sheet

Date: _____

Topic: _____

Mode: ☐ Consecutive   ☐ Sight Translation   ☐ Simultaneous

Accuracy and Completeness	**Did the interpreter** ☐ Leave content out? ☐ Add content? ☐ Distort meaning? ☐ Communicate the message?	☐ A little ☐ A lot ☐ A little ☐ A lot ☐ A little ☐ A lot ☐ A little ☐ A lot *Comments:*
Language	**Were there problems with** ☐ Grammar? ☐ Syntax? ☐ Terminology? ☐ Pronunciation?	☐ A little ☐ A lot ☐ A little ☐ A lot ☐ A little ☐ A lot ☐ A little ☐ A lot *Comments:*
Delivery	**Was the delivery** ☐ Confident? ☐ Smooth? ☐ Understandable? ☐ Hesitant? **Did the interpreter** ☐ Stutter? ☐ Backtrack/start over?	☐ A little ☐ A lot ☐ A little ☐ A lot ☐ A little ☐ A lot ☐ A little ☐ A lot ☐ A little ☐ A lot ☐ A little ☐ A lot *Comments:*
Use of Strategies	**Did the interpreter** ☐ Analyze content? ☐ Restructure sentences? ☐ Problem-solve? ☐ Show background knowledge? ☐ Lag just a little behind the speaker? (for simultaneous only)	☐ A little ☐ A lot ☐ A little ☐ A lot ☐ A little ☐ A lot ☐ A little ☐ A lot *Comments:*

Reflective practice role plays

Role play #1: NICU (English-Spanish)

Patient:		¿Doctor, dónde está mi bebé? ¿Qué pasó en la sala de partos? Me pujé fuerte—el doctor me dijo 'puje una vez más, puje fuerte" y lo hice. Después me sentí un alivio y hubo un momento de silencio, que para mí era un eternidad, y empecé a escuchar ruidos del bebé, no llanto, sino ruidos y entonces de repente vi un alboroto y mucho movimiento y sonaban todas las máquinas…	Doctor, where is my baby? What happened in the delivery room? I gave a big push—the doctor told me "one more big push" and I did that. Then I felt some relief and there was a moment of silence, which felt like eternity to me, and then I started to hear all these noises, not baby cries, but noises. Then all of sudden there was a commotion and movement and all the machines were beeping…
Pediatrician:	Yes, I know everything happened so fast, but let me try to explain what happened, at least what happened with the baby. I was one of the doctors in the delivery room. I'm a pediatrician, not an OB, but I think the OB will be in soon because I saw her at the nurse's station. Or the nurse will be in, I'm not sure. Anyway…		
Patient:		Dígame, doctor, por favor! Como está mi bebe. ¡No entiendo nada de lo que está pasando! Me dijeron que es una niña, verdad?	Tell me, please, doctor, how is my baby? I don't understand anything that is going on here. They told me it was a girl, right?
Pediatrician:	Yes, it's a girl and she's in the NICU right now. I just came down from there. She is stable now but we need to keep a close eye on her.		

Patient:		¿Qué pasó ¿Qué fueron esos ruidos, como ronquidos, como cuando alguién ronca feo?	What happened? What were those sounds, like grunts, like when someone snores a lot.
Pediatrician:	Your baby has RDS or respiratory distress syndrome. In other words, she had problems breathing right after birth and that was what you heard.		
Patient:		¿Cómo sabe que fue eso, algo que suena tan grave, y no que solo ahogaba en algo, como que cuando tiene algo en la garganta, como flema? No puedo creer que está tan enferma—sé que estoy hecho pedazos yo, pero no ella, no mi nena…	How do you know that's what it is, that sounds so terrible, and not just something that she was choking on, like when you have something in your throat? I can't believe she's so sick—I know that I'm all messed up, but not her, not my baby, she can't be…
Pediatrician:	Well, she was short of breath and making the sounds you heard. So that's a sign that there is a problem. Then her lips and face started to turn blue and that is another serious sign. Her nostrils were flaring, she was breathing fast, then not breathing, then breathing or grunting again. All this together means that she was in respiratory distress.		
Patient:		¿Pero, de qué viene eso? No me dijeron que el bebé venía con un problema, solo yo era la que tenía todos los problemas.	But what is that from? They never told me that the baby had any problems—I was the one who had all the problems.

Pediatrician:	Again, I'm the pediatrician and I deal with babies, not pregnancies. These types of breathing problems are common in preemies, and your baby was born at 31 weeks, which is premature. What I understand is that your blood pressure spiked and they had to induce labor. You had gestational diabetes too, right?		
Patient:		Si, y tomaba insulina.	Yes, and I took insulin.
Pediatrician:	OK, that's something else that is common when we see this condition in babies. So, the diabetes, the induction, and the fact the baby was premature are all factors in the baby's breathing problems.		
Patient:		Pero cómo está mi nena, no me ha dicho nada de ella todavía. ¿Estará bien ella? Sí no pudo respirar, ¿eso le hizo algún daño?	But how is my baby, you haven't told me anything about her yet. Will she be OK? If she couldn't breathe, did that do any damage to her?
Pediatrician:	She is stable and she is in the NICU under observation. She seems fine for now, but we won't know if there are any long-term effects until later, but, honestly, I don't expect there to be. She will get worse over the next two or three days and then she will slowly start to get better.		
Patient:		Bueno, gracias, ¡Que bueno! Gracias a Dios.	OK, thank you. How wonderful! Thank God.

Pediatrician:	We did some blood tests to rule out any infection and we might need to do a chest X-ray but I am not sure. We have to see how she does over the next couple of hours.		
Patient:		Está bien. ¿La van a traer aquí para estar conmigo?	OK, Are they going to bring her here to be with me?
Pediatrician:	No, we can't do that. She needs to stay in the NICU under observation. There's a nurse there who is checking her temperature, pulse and oxygen levels, and also her IV fluids and nutrition. You will be able to go see her though.		
Patient:		(sighs) ¡Que bueno! ¿Cuando?	(sighs) Fantastic! When?
Pediatrician:	I am not sure yet. You have been through a lot. The nurse will be in soon and you can talk to her about that.		
Patient:		Está bien. Gracias Doctor, gracias por todo la información. Me siento mucho más tranquila ahora. Gracias.	OK, doctor, thank you for all the information. I feel much calmer now. Thanks.
Pediatrician:	You're welcome, and I am glad to hear that. Just a few more things. When you go up to the NICU, please don't be scared—the baby is in an incubator to keep her warm and has a bunch of tubes in her.		
Patient:		¿Sondas? ¿Para qué?	Tubes? What for?

Pediatrician:	Well, she has IV liquids and a CPAP. The CPAP is a device that sends air into lungs to keep her airways open and this way the baby won't need a ventilator. We also did some blood tests so she has a little bandage on both her heels where the nurse drew blood.		
Patient:		Solo quiero abrazar a mi bebe y tocarle la cara.	I just want to hold my baby and caress her face.
Pediatrician:	I don't see any reason to worry right now. Like I said, there is a nurse right with your baby and we also have a pediatric pulmonologist in the unit as well—oh, here is your OB and the nurse. Goodbye for now and I will try to check back in later.		
Patient:		Gracias, adios.	Thank you. Goodbye.

Role play #2: The infected tooth (English-Spanish)

Dentist:	Mr. Padilla I just reviewed the X-ray the tech took of the tooth that is bothering you. You have a really deep cavity there, and on top of that the tooth is infected.		
Patient:		¡Doctora, el dolor es horrible! No he dormido durante dos noches seguidas, no puedo ni comer ni tomar nada. Cualquier cosa que toca el diente me da una punzada que me dan ganas de gritar hasta el cielo.	Doctor, the pain is just terrible! I haven't slept in two straight nights. I can't eat or drink anything because if anything touches the tooth, I get a stabbing pain that makes me want to scream out in pain.
Dentist:	I know, a tooth infection is very painful. When I tried to examine you, I couldn't even touch the tooth with my sickle probe.		
Patient:		¿Qué se puede hacer? No puedo pasar otra noche así.	What can I do? I can't spend another night like that.
Dentist:	Well I can't do anything if I can't even touch the tooth. So, first we need to get rid of the infection. I am going to give you antibiotics and I want you to take them for seven days.		
Patient:		Está bien. ¿Me dará algo para el dolor?	OK. Will you give me something for the pain?
Dentist:	Yes, I will give you something for the pain, but it is a narcotic, so I have to give you a prescription. I can't just send you to the pharmacy. Take it only as needed, and don't drive or work while you are taking it, because it will make you sleepy.		

Patient:		Está bien. No estoy trabajando ahora de todos modos.	That's fine. I'm not working now anyway.
Dentist:	The inflammation should disappear in about three days, but you need to finish all the antibiotics.		
Patient:		Termino todos los antibióticos aunque me sienta mejor, entiendo.	I'll finish all the antibiotics even though I feel better. I understand.
Dentist:	Yes, that is important. We will give you an appointment to come back next week. The cavity looks pretty bad, so I think you're going to need a root canal.		
Patient:		¡No me digas eso! Eso es carísimo.	Don't tell me that! That's so expensive.
Dentist:	I won't know for sure until I can examine the tooth better. I might be able to put a temporary filling in, but that only lasts for about two months or so. The temporary filling has some medicine in it.		
Patient:		Si doctora, hagamos eso primero, a ver si me compongo así.	Yes, doctor, let's do that first to see if I get better that way.
Dentist:	All right. If I put in a temporary filling and you don't have any more pain, I can put a permanent filling in and that will buy you some time. I still think you will need a root canal eventually.		

Patient:		Está bien. Tengo planes de volver a mi país el año que viene y puedo hacerme la endodoncia allá porque así me saldrá más barato en mi país. Si es que se puede hacer algo ahora, eso me daría tiempo de esperar hasta el año que viene; se lo agradecería muchísimo.	Fine. I'm planning to go back to my country next year and I can do the root canal there since it will be cheaper for me there. If you could do something for me now, something so that I could make it to next year, I would really appreciate it.
Dentist:	Well, we will see next week. Mr. Padilla, you came here three years ago and I told you that you had a cavity on that tooth and you never came back.		
Patient:		Yo sé doctora, es que se me hace difícil venir por el trabajo.	I know, doctor. It is difficult for me to get here because of work.
Dentist:	We also have office hours on Tuesday and Thursday nights and Saturday mornings. And you can always come any day as an emergency at 8 a.m. or 12:30 p.m. You can see any of my colleagues for help.		
Patient:		Está bien doctora, gracias por la información.	OK, doctor, thank you for the information.
Dentist:	This is what happens when you let a cavity go on for too long. If cost is an issue, it is much more expensive to get a root canal, a post and core, and then a crown, than to get one cavity filled.		
Patient:		Sí, entiendo, doctora. Uno no piensa así en el momento.	Yes, I understand. I didn't think about that at that time.

Dentist:	Here is the prescription for the pain, and I also just gave you the prescription for the antibiotics there as well instead of sending it electronically. Make an appointment for next week on your way out. Then we will see what you will need.		
Patient:		Sí, doctora, y disculpe.	Yes, doctor, and I apologize.
Dentist:	You are going to need a cleaning and a checkup too. You should also make an appointment for that as well on your way out.		
Patient:		Está bien doctora, gracias. Lo voy a hacer.	OK, doctor, thank you. I'll take care of it.

Role play #3: The patient who went to many doctors (English-Spanish)

Internist:	Ms. Godínez, you haven't been here in about eight months. The last time you were here was in August, last year.		
Patient:		Sí doctora, lo que pasa es que estuve en Nueva York para cuidar a un amigo de la familia que vive allí. Desafortunadamente, él se enfermó y, puesto que vive solo, no había quién lo cuidara. Entonces, de ley tuve que irme allá y al final, pasé todo el invierno en su casa.	Yes, doctor. This is what happened: I was in New York taking care of a friend of the family that lives in the city. Unfortunately, he got sick and since he lives by himself, there was no one to take care of him. So I had to leave for the city and, in the end, I spent the whole winter at his apartment.
Internist:	I understand all that, but you never came back. Ms. Godínez, do you understand that you have diabetes and that it is a very serious condition?		
Patient:		Sí, entiendo.	Yes, I understand.
Internist:	Well, when you came in the first time, your sugar was really out of control, 300, 370, 450; that is not good. Your hemoglobin A1c was 12 and that is very high. Do you remember how you felt?		
Patient:		Sí, doctora, sí me acuerdo. Y perdóneme… por no haber venido.	Yes, doctor, yes, I remember. And, I'm sorry…
Internist:	Well I understand that things happen, but if you don't come in, I can't take care of you. Your sugar is high again. What medicines are you taking now?		

Patient:		Tomo dos de 500mgs dos veces al día. Eso es para el azúcar.	I take two pills, 500mgs each, twice a day. That's for my sugar.
Internist:	All right, but who changed that? The last note I have for you is that you were supposed to take one pill twice a day, so 1,000 mgs total a day. Then you were supposed to come in a month to see if it was working.		
Patient:		No pude venir porque me fui a Nueva York. Mi amigo se puso peor mal y yo no podía dejarlo solo. Además no podía pagar el transporte de allá para acá. Después el clima cambió y empezó a nevar bastante. Entonces, yo no pude hacer nada.	I wasn't able to come back in because I left for New York. My friend got worse, and I couldn't leave him alone. Besides, I couldn't afford the trip down here. Then it got cold and started to snow a lot. I couldn't do anything about it.
Internist:	When did you stop taking your medicines?		
Patient:		Pues, creo que se me terminaron en Octubre o a mediados de Septiembre. No estoy segura.	Well, I think I ran out in October or the middle of September. I'm not sure.
Internist:	What happened after you stopped taking your medicines? How did you feel? Did you have any nausea or vomiting?		
Patient:		Pues, en el principio, estaba bien, o sea, me sentía bien. Pero después empecé a sentirme como me sentía antes. Me daba náusea, pero porque el departamento de mi amigo tenía muchas cucarachas, pensé que era por eso—no estoy acostumbrada a vivir así. Él vive en uno de esos edificios grandotes en el Bronx.	Well, at the beginning I was fine, I mean, I felt fine. But then, I started to feel like I felt before. I had nausea, but because the apartment had many roaches I thought it was because of that—I'm not used to living like that. He lives in one of those huge buildings in the Bronx.

Internist:	So did you have a lot of nausea? What other symptoms did you have? Were you more thirsty than normal? Were you urinating more frequently?		
Patient:		Si, todo eso, doctora. Me di cuenta que era por la diabetes porque me sentía igual que cuando vine a verla a usted el año pasado. Cuando mi amigo me vio así tan enferma, él me llevo con su doctor en el Bronx. Él me dio nuevos medicamentos y me aumentó la dosis también.	Yes, doctor, I had all those symptoms. I realized it was because of the diabetes because I felt the same way I did when I came in to see you last year. When my friend saw I was so sick, he took me to see his doctor there in the Bronx. That doctor gave me more of the medicine I was taking before and upped the dose.
Internist:	Oh, I see. Now I understand. So you went to see another doctor. I cannot treat you if you plan on going to different doctors. He changed your medicines, and he changed the dose. I don't know if he did any tests. I think you'll have to decide who you want to be your doctor. Do you plan on staying here in New Jersey?		
Patient:		(to the interpreter) Parece que está bien molesta conmigo. Explíquele que cuando mi amigo me ofreció llevarme a ver al médico; yo no podía decirle "no" porque eso sería un insulto. Usted sabe cómo es en nuestra cultura—no se puede despreciar la ayuda. Pero, tampoco quería insultar a la doctora. Yo voy a quedarme aquí con ella.	(to the interpreter) It looks like the doctor is very upset with me. Make her understand that when my friend offered to take me to the doctor when I was sick, I couldn't say "no" because that would be insulting. You know how it is in our culture—when someone wants to help you, you can't turn him down. But I didn't want to insult the doctor either. I'll stay here.

Internist:	I'm not upset, Ms. Godínez…Ofelia, I'm not upset with you. Diabetes is very serious, with your sugar so high you could end up in the hospital, it can damage your kidneys and your eyes and you can lose sensation in your feet. But you can avoid all that if you just come in when you're supposed to.		
Patient:		Está bien, doctora, lo voy a hacer. Entiendo lo grave que es tener diabetes.	OK, doctor, I'll stay on top of all that. I understand how serious diabetes is.
Internist:	Well, your A1c is 12.6, so it's gone up. I'm thinking we might need to start insulin. I understand that you had to go to the city to take care of a family member and when he wanted to return the favor, you couldn't say no. But we need to get back on track now. Let me examine your feet now.		
Patient:		Está bien. ¿Me quito los calcetines y los zapatos?	Right. Should I take off my socks and shoes?
Internist:	Yes, please. What are these marks on your legs?		
Patient:		Mi amigo dice que son las chinches. Su departamento tenía eso también.	They say it's from bedbugs. His apartment had them too.
Internist:	They look infected. Do they bother you?		
Patient:		Sí, me pican mucho. A veces me sale sangre, pero ya se están secando desde que regresé a mi casa.	Yes, they itch and sometimes they also bleed, but they're drying up since I came back down here.

Internist:	Well, I don't like the way they look. I'm going to give you an antibiotic cream to put on them. We're also going to get some blood tests. I'm going to talk to my attending to see if we should start insulin or not. I'll be back in a minute.		
Patient:		Está bien, doctora y gracias por entenderme. Una vez más, nunca fue mi intención molestarla. Perdón.	OK, doctor, and thanks for understanding. Again, I never meant to upset you.

Role play #4: Education: Bullying victim[7]

Assistant principal:	Good morning, Ms. Martinez. My name is John Smith, one of the assistant principals of this school. What can I do for you today?		
Parent:		Si, mire, vengo echando chispas, por lo que esos gringos le hicieron a mi patojito. Y yo quiero saber qué es lo que usted va a hacer al respecto.	Yes, well, I'm just fuming through my nostrils about what those guys did to my little boy. And I want to know what you're going to do about it.
Assistant principal:	No, I'm sorry I don't know what happened to Manuel. Please tell me.		
Parent:		Vea, ayer después de la escuela mi patojo llegó a la casa llorando y me dijo que dos gringos de esta escuela lo maltrataron y lo golpearon con una pelota en sus cositas en la parada del autobús, y mi patojo pasó toda la noche con dolor. Esta mañana cuando me he despertado sus cositas están bien hinchadas y le duelen mucho.	Well, yesterday after school my son came home crying and told me that two guys from this school picked on him, and hit him with a ball in his private parts at the bus stop. My son was in pain all night. This morning when I woke up, his private parts were all swollen and they hurt him bad.
Assistant principal:	I'm very sorry that this happened to your son. Is Manuel here in school today?		

[7]Adapted from Bancroft and Rubio-Fitzpatrick (2011), *The Community Interpreter: A Comprehensive Training Manual*, 5th ed. Columbia, MD: Culture & Language Press, pp. 14-16.

Parent:		No! Que no ve que ni siquiera puede caminar. Se quedó en la casa dormido mientras yo vine a quejarme. Porque yo quiero que usted castigue a esos dos niños.	No! He can't even walk. He stayed home sleeping while I came to complain, because I want you to punish those two boys.
Assistant principal:	I understand, Ms. Martinez. You have a right to be upset, and I assure you these boys will be punished for what they did. Now, can you please tell me if your son told you the names of these boys?		
Parent:		Sí, aquí los tengo apuntados en este pedazo de papel. Vea usted, yo no sé como pronunciarlos, así que tome el papel.	Yes, I have them written down on this piece of paper. Here, I don't know how to pronounce them, so take this paper.
Assistant principal:	I want you to know that the school has a strict policy against bullying and fighting. The students are well aware of this policy and they know this type of behavior will not be tolerated.		
Parent:		Si, pero quiero que sepa que ésta no es la primera vez que pasa. Manuelito, como yo le llamo, me ha dicho que siempre le están haciendo burla porque es gordito y también me le llaman sobrenombres constantemente. Mi patojo ya ni quiere venir a la escuela por eso. Por eso es que yo estoy muy enojada y decidí venir hoy.	Yes, but I want you to know that this isn't the first time this has happened. Manuelito, as I call him, told me that they're always making fun of him because he's chubby, and always calling him names. My son doesn't even want to go to school because of this. That's why I'm so angry and I decided to come in today.

Assistant principal:	Thank you. You did the right thing by coming this morning and letting us know this was happening.		
Parent:		Ahora, yo necesito llevarlo al doctor para que me lo chequee, pero no tengo seguro y tampoco, estoy trabajando. Dígame usted cómo le hago. Sin dinero ni seguro ningún médico quiere atender a uno. Yo estoy aquí sola, y tampoco tengo marido que me ayude con los gastos. La migra lo deportó hace un año y no ha vuelto.	Now I need to take him to the doctor to be checked out, but I don't have insurance and I'm not working. What am I supposed to do? Without money or insurance no doctor wants to see you. I'm here alone, and I don't have a husband who helps me with expenses. Immigration deported him a year ago and he hasn't come back.
Assistant principal:	I understand your concern. Please let me talk to the school nurse and see if she can refer you to a clinic nearby that can see your son right away. Hopefully it will be free of charge or at low cost to you. Would that be okay with you?		
Parent:		Por supuesto, señor, si usted me hace el favor le agradeceré mucho. Quiero asegurarme que mi patojo no tenga nada grave.	Of course, sir, I'd be real grateful if you'd do me that favor. I want to be sure that my son isn't seriously hurt.
Assistant principal:	Again, I'm sorry about what happened to your son. I assure you there will be consequences for the boys' behavior. Thank you for coming, and tell your son we hope he gets better soon.		

Role play #5: The domestic violence hotline call (English only)

Domestic violence victim:		(whispering in a shaky voice): Hello?
Advocate:	(*soothing voice*) Hello, my name is Silvia, how can I help you?	
Domestic violence victim:		I think, um, I think I need some help.
Advocate:	Are you in any immediate danger? Have you called 911?	
Domestic violence victim:		(whispering in a shaky voice): No, no police. He would be very angry if the police showed up. I just have a few questions. Do I have to give my name?
Advocate:	No you're fine. You can be anonymous if that's what you prefer. Can you give me a telephone number, though? I'm just asking your name in case we're disconnected.	
Domestic violence victim:		My first name, it's Ana. I can give you my phone number, but no, if we're disconnected you can't call me back!
Advocate:	Is there anyone else in the house with you?	
Domestic violence victim:		My children, yes.
Advocate	Ana, you sound afraid.	
Domestic violence victim:		(whispering in a shaky voice): My man, Tony, he's been drinking all day, yelling at me, and—and he hit me hard.
Advocate:	Is Tony there at the moment?	
Domestic violence victim:		No, not right now, he left about 30 minutes ago. My two kids are with me, Delia and Omar. My friend Gina said I should call you. This is happening more often since he lost his job.

Advocate:	(*calm voice*): Ana, it's nice that your friend Gina is letting you know about us. Can you describe what happened?	
Domestic violence victim:		(still whispering but less shaky voice): About an hour ago, he hit me on my face with his fist and I have a black eye, busted lip and maybe a broken nose. He's been feeling kinda blue and out of sorts for months now.
Advocate	(*very calm voice*): Is this the first time he hit you?	
Domestic violence victim:		(still whispering but less shaky voice): Well, no, he slapped me around before, but this is the first time he went crazy. Mostly he pushes me, slaps my face, calls me names like stupid or lazy, and threatens to leave me and the kids. But this time after he slapped me, he punched me, he beat me, he used his fists and when I fell down and he kicked me he wouldn't stop until he saw I was bleeding.
Advocate	(*remains utterly calm*): Have you had any medical care?	
Domestic violence victim:		(almost crying) No, I'm fine, I'll be fine.
Advocate:	Did he hit Delia and Omar too? How old are they?	
Domestic violence victim:		No, no, he doesn't hit the kids, only me, but this time he was so mad that I was afraid he would start hitting them too. Delia's four and Omar is seven. They heard it all and started crying to their Daddy to stop. He yelled at them and then stormed out of the house. He got in his truck and drove off.
Advocate:	Ana, how long exactly has this been going on?	

Domestic violence victim:		We've been together for many years now and he was always strict and he yelled a lot if he got angry, but the hitting started when he lost his job. It's been over a year and he can't find another job so he drinks and gets mean. (voice starts getting louder) What should I do? It's getting dangerous and if he hits the kids…
Advocate:	Well, whatever it is that you want to do—if you want to go to the hospital or leave your home and get to a safe place or seek counseling for you or for him— whatever services you're looking for I can help you with right now.	
Domestic violence victim:		I—it's getting so dangerous for me and my kids. I think I want to leave.
Advocate:	If you're looking at coming to see us and get to a safe place, we can do that right now if you have 15 minutes. We can do over-the-phone intake and there's other places we can refer you to as well. We also offer legal advocacy services that will help you with any children's services you need or any other legal matters. All our services are at no cost to you and they're confidential. And by the way this is a 24-hour hotline, you can call us back at any time. Do you feel safe to talk for 15 minutes?	
Domestic violence victim:		(hesitant voice): But I have no papers, will you still help me?
Advocate:	(calm voice): No problem. We serve anyone regardless of race, ethnicity, gender, religion, income, disability, or sexual orientation. We can even help you apply for other services you need, depending on your financial qualification and legal status. I'm not saying it's easy without papers, but there are some things we can help you get, like shelter.	

Domestic violence victim:		I don't know. I don't know if I have 15 minutes to talk. Maybe I should leave now? Can you tell me where to go?
Advocate:	Ana, I can, but here's what you need to take. If you feel you can do this safely and leave home before he comes back, be sure to take all your important documents with you. I mean your Social Security card, your birth certificate, your insurance card, any kind of valid ID or anything that an abuser can use or hold against you. Take your tax forms and any important papers. Do you have those on hand?	
Domestic violence victim:		And if he comes back before I leave right now?
Advocate:	You can always call 911 for help. But if you plan to leave in the next day do you have a safe place to stay? Do you have a family member you trust to go stay with that Tony doesn't know about? Because we will absolutely help you.	
Domestic violence victim:		I'm not sure, I think he's at the door, I locked him out. He's knocking I'm scared…
Advocate:	Ma'am, are you in any immediate danger?	
Domestic violence victim:		I—I don't know.
Advocate:	Ma'am, if you feel like you're in any immediate danger I advise you to hang up the phone right now and dial 911. If you feel like he's going to hurt you just dial the number out and hang up. The police will come right away.	

Instructions

- Working individually, listen to the interpreting you recorded in Learning Activity 1.6 (b).
- Write down one goal with two objectives to work on improving areas of weakness in your performance.
- Remember that a goal states the *general* improvement you want to see (better delivery, improved grammar and/or better accuracy).
- The objectives give the specific, measurable steps you will take to reach that goal.
- Write your goal and objectives following the structure below.

<u>Sample</u>

Goal: *I want to improve grammar in my non-native working language when I interpret consecutively.*

Objective 1: *Using class materials, once a week I will record myself practicing the same role-play three times in a row, each time focusing exclusively on using correct grammar when I interpret. I will listen back to my recording after each practice, note down any grammatical errors, and work to correct them during the next playback of the role play.*

Objective 2: *Once a week, I will listen to a podcast in my non-native language and note down correct grammar structures and use of terminology.*

Objective 3: *This year, I will take one higher-level course in the grammar of my non-native language either in a class setting or online or through self-study materials.*

Goal

_____

_____

Objective 1

_____

_____

_____

Objective 2

_____

_____

_____

Objective 3

_____

_____

_____

LEARNING OBJECTIVES

After completing this chapter and its corresponding exercises, the learner will be able to:

OBJECTIVE 2.1	**Stages of the Encounter** Identify and describe the three stages of a typical community interpreting assignment: pre-encounter, interpreted encounter and post-encounter.
OBJECTIVE 2.2	**Four Protocols for Community Interpreting** Discuss and practice four protocols for community interpreting: positioning, professional introductions, direct speech (first person) and turn-taking management.
OBJECTIVE 2.3	**Memory Skills** *(a)* Describe three memory processes: encoding, storage and retrieval. *(b)* Practice three cognitive strategies: mnemonics, chunking and imagery.
OBJECTIVE 2.4	**Message Transfer Skills** *(a)* Practice three cognitive processes: anticipating, multitasking and message analysis. *(b)* Explore two interpreting skills-building strategies: parroting (shadowing) and paraphrasing.
OBJECTIVE 2.5	**Modes, Summarization and Mode Switching** *(a)* Engage in three modes of interpreting: consecutive, simultaneous and sight translation. *(b)* Understand the rationale, skills and requirements for summarization. *(c)* Define, describe and practice mode-switching.
OBJECTIVE 2.6	**Note Taking for Consecutive Interpreting** *(a)* Understand the rationale, skills and requirements for consecutive note taking. *(b)* Practice three effective techniques for note taking: apply a simplified Rozan technique and develop symbol and abbreviation systems.

Learning Objective 2.1

After completing this section and its corresponding exercises, the learner will be able to:

- Identify and describe the three stages of a typical community interpreting assignment: pre-encounter, encounter and post-encounter.

 Learning Activity 2.1(a): Prepare for the Assignment

Instructions

- Look at the three stages of the interpreted encounter: pre-encounter (preparation and briefing); encounter (introductions, interpreting, intervening/mediating) and post-encounter (debriefing and analysis): which parts are hardest? Why does planning matter?
- Select one of the medical role plays in Learning Activity 1.6 (b), unless your instructor directs you to a different role play.
- Imagine that you will have to interpret for this type of assignment.
- In the blank lines provided write down what preparation you will need to do for all parts of the encounter to go smoothly: discuss specific strategies.
- Now read pp. 119-120 of your textbook about pre-encounter. Add anything you wish to what you wrote below.
- Finally, how would a hospital setting affect your preparation? Note down at least three ways in which your preparation for a hospital assignment might be different compared to a healthcare interpreting assignment in a non-hospital setting (such as a health department, counseling center or mobile clinic).

_____

_____

_____

_____

_____

_____

 Learning Activity 2.1(b): Debriefing Role Play

Instructions (in-person interpreting)

- Work in pairs. One person will play a hospital social worker; the other will play an interpreter.
- Imagine that you have just interpreted for a family conference in a hospital where the parents learned that their child will die. In addition to the doctor and a nurse, the social worker was present.
- You performed professionally, but you can see the social worker has noticed that you were disturbed.

- After the meeting, you ask if you could speak to the social worker briefly about the encounter and she agrees.
- *The person who plays the social worker will read from the script below. (The social worker is referred to there as the "debriefer.") <u>The interpreter will not look at the script but will make up natural answers</u>.*

Note: Most community interpreters *do not get a debrief* unless (or even if) they ask for one. However, if you work for a language company or interpret for a therapist or other licensed clinician (including a clinical social worker, psychologist or counselor), you might request and receive a debrief. This role play shows you what a professional debrief can look like. The intention is to give you a "feel" for a debrief.

Instructions (for remote interpreting by telephone or video, whether by hospital staff interpreters, contract interpreters or language company call-center interpreters)

- Work in pairs. One person will play a staff member at a language company or hospital who performs debriefing of telephone interpreters; the other will play an interpreter calling by telephone.
- Imagine that you have just interpreted *remotely* or *in person* for a hospital patient shot by her husband, who then killed himself in front of her. You were engaged by a language company and interpreted by telephone or video.
- You performed professionally, and forced yourself to get through the session.
- Afterward, knowing that debriefers are available, you call up the language company and asked if you could speak to someone briefly about the encounter.
- *The person who plays the language company or hospital debriefer will read from the same script below as for the instructions above, but in this case the interpreter will imagine that he or she is speaking not to a hospital social worker but to a language company staff member offering a debrief by telephone. Note: as in the instructions above, <u>the interpreter will not look at the script but will make up natural answers</u>.*

Note: Some telephone and video interpreting companies and even hospitals do offer interpreter debriefing for stressful medical and other high-stakes interpreted encounters. This is becoming a little more common in the United States, for example. However, having a debriefer available for interprters is not yet an international norm. Because most interpreters are unaware that such resources are available, they should inquire about them when they work for language companies and other interpreting service providers (ISPs), including hospital call centers and hospital interpreting departments.

Debriefing role play

Debriefer:	It sounds like you found that assignment pretty intense—how did it go for you?	
Interpreter:		
Debriefer:	Well, I'm concerned what you need to do to take care of yourself. Do you need to go for a walk or do you just need to be with your family or friends?	
Interpreter:		
Debriefer:	That sounds fine. What about interpreting? Do you feel ready to go to your next assignment, or should we try to see if we can find another interpreter for that one?	
Interpreter:		
Debriefer:	Well, maybe think about who you can talk to about this, and how to relax. Obviously you're not going to give any confidential details, but you might want to talk about how you feel with another interpreter you really trust, or maybe a family member or friend, someone who usually helps you feel like yourself so you feel you can get back to normal as soon as possible. When do you think you'll be home?	
Interpreter:		
Debriefer:	I see. So what do you plan to do first, right now?	
Interpreter:		
Debriefer:	And what are you going to do after that?	
Interpreter:		
Debriefer:	All right, that sounds good. Just remember— keep this session confidential, but if you want to share your feelings about it, as long as it's someone you trust, that's usually okay. You don't have to keep your feelings confidential!	

Learning Objective 2.2

After completing this section and its corresponding exercises, the learner will be able to:

- Discuss and practice four protocols for community interpreting: positioning, professional introductions, direct speech (first person) and turn-taking management.

 Learning Activity 2.2(a): Where Would You Sit or Stand?

Instructions

- In groups of three, read one of the two sets of scenarios below (general or medical).
- **Medical interpreters should select the medical scenarios.**
- For each scenario, decide on one of the positioning choices suggested.
- For each scenario, justify your choice of position.

Post-activity instructions

- Your instructor will now recruit three volunteers to portray (without speaking) an interpreter, a patient and a doctor.
- The instructor will place them first in a triangle (the preferred position in Europe for community interpreting). Observe that position. As a group, discuss its advantages and disadvantages.
- The instructor will then place the interpreter slightly behind the patient. Observe that position (the preferred/default position for many medical interpreters in the United States). As a group, discuss the advantages and disadvantages of this position.
- The instructor will then place the interpreter slightly behind the provider. Observe this position, which is one used by many medical and community interpreters. As a group, discuss the advantages and disadvantages of this position.
- Now, as a group, discuss the reality: that no one position is ideal. Often, the interpreter's position will have to change based on the room, the number of participants, the type of service being delivered and many other factors. So what will each interpreter do to decide what position to take when walking into a room?
- Now answer the question below.

What is your first priority when selecting an appropriate position for community or medical interpreting?

_____

_____

_____

Positioning scenarios: general

- A parent-teacher meeting
- A meeting between a refugee and an income support worker in a government social service office
- A meeting at a teenager's home with the teen's parole officer
- A senior center meeting where participants listen to a nutritionist discussing cooking for diabetics
- A social worker meeting a husband, wife, uncle and two grown children in a small office
- A meeting to address special education services for a child's learning disability at a round table where the following are seated: a teacher, an assistant principal, a reading specialist, an occupational therapist and a speech therapist

Positioning scenarios: medical

- A routine healthcare appointment
- A dental appointment
- An appointment with a therapist at a sexual assault center
- A nurse home visit in the patient's living room where the interpreter is invited to sit on the sofa
- A hospital operating room
- A doctor's examination room so tiny that there is no place for you to sit and the patient is lying on an examination bed against the wall
- A child lying down in a school health room while the health aide attends to him
- A prenatal class. (You are interpreting for a husband and wife. The instructor is up front. The wife is lying on the floor and the husband is kneeling beside her.)

 Learning Activity 2.2(b): A Professional Introduction

Instructions

- Work in pairs. It does not matter if your partner has the same language pair(s).
- First, read the sample introduction below. In the blank lines that follow, add any important item you wish to include.
- Now take turns practicing your introduction to your partner in both (or all) your working languages.
- *Try to complete your introduction in both working languages in fewer than 20 seconds!*

1. What would *you* add to this sample introduction used by many community and medical interpreters in the United States?

My name is ... and I'll be your interpreter today.
1. *I'll be interpreting everything that is said (or signed) today.*[8]
2. *I'll keep everything confidential.*
3. *Please speak (or sign) directly to each other, not to me.*
4. *Please pause when I give this signal [demonstrate the signal], to let me interpret.*

---

[8]Sign language interpreters have typically had extensive education and training; they may have their own style of professional introduction. If so they can demonstrate and/or practice their own introduction.

Note: There is no standard signal used by all community or medical interpreters to ask service users or providers to pause. Interpreters use many different hand signals; some cough, lean forward and make eye contact or lift a pen. Find the signal that works best for you.

Write down anything you would like to add to the sample introduction above. (For example, you could add, *Please don't state anything you don't want me to interpret, because I have to interpret everything you say.*)

_____

_____

_____

 Learning Activity 2.2(c): Turn-Taking Practice

Instructions

- In groups of three, take turns practicing the role play below.
- One person will play the doctor, one person will play the patient and one person will play the interpreter.
- The interpreter *will not look at the script.*
- Each time someone in the role play speaks (or signs) too long, *interrupt* that person with an appropriate signal so that you can interpret accurately.
- When your instructor says, "Switch interpreter," let a different person play the interpreter.

Medical role play for turn-taking: Consent for LEEP

Gynecologist:	Hi, Ms. Quintana, it's nice to see you again. I asked you to come back today so we can talk about the results of the colposcopy and the biopsy that we did a few weeks back. And, I would like to talk about our next steps.		
Patient:		Hola. No hay problema, de todos modos yo tenía que venir al hospital hoy por una cita de seguimiento que tuvo mi hijo.	Hi. It's not a problem—I had to come to the hospital anyway because my son had a follow-up appointment today.
Gynecologist:	Oh. Well, I hope everything is OK with him.		
Patient:		Mi hijo está bien, gracias. El cardiólogo lo chequea cada seis meses porque tiene un soplo. Así que yo ya estaba en esta área de los pacientes ambulatorios, ya me la conozco de memoria, no sólo por usted sino también por mi hijo.	My boy is fine, thanks. The cardiologist sees him every six months to check his murmur. So, I have been already in the outpatient unit anyway—I know it by heart.
Gynecologist:	Before we talk about our next steps, I like to review what we have done so far and what each of those steps mean. OK?		
Patient:		Bueno, lo que usted diga.	OK, whatever you say.
Gynecologist:	You had a pap smear done and it was abnormal. Then we did a colposcopy and we took a biopsy. Do you remember that?		
Patient:		Claro que me acuerdo de eso. Si yo estaba bien incómoda porque me ardía mucho cuando usted me echó el líquido en la matriz. La biopsia me dolió un poco y sentí como piquetes, como que algo me pinchaba. Entonces sí, sí me acuerdo de todo eso muy bien.	Of course I remember. I was real uncomfortable because it burned when you put that liquid inside me. The biopsy hurt and it stung, like something was pinching me. So, yeah, yeah I remember that all too well.

Gynecologist:	Yes, that all sounds about normal. We sent the sample we took out when we did the biopsy to the lab for analysis and I have the results. This is what I want to discuss with you.		
Patient:		Ok, dígame entonces. ¿Tengo que repetir la colposcopía? Porque eso es lo que siempre pasa. ¿Verdad?	Ok, well, tell me. Do I have to do the colposcopy again? That is what usually happens right?
Gynecologist:	Well in some cases, yes, but not in yours. The results show changes in cells of the cervix and these cells could become cancerous. In your case, the changes are significant and we need to do something soon.		
Patient:		¿Qué? ¡O sea que tengo cáncer!	What? You mean I have cancer!
Gynecologist:	No, Ms. Quintana, you don't have cancer yet, but we do need to take care of these cells. Let me explain. There is a virus called the HPV virus that all women have in their vagina. In some women, this virus doesn't cause any problems, but in other women, it causes these changes that can develop into cervical cancer.		
Patient:		¿Hay algún tratamiento? ¿Puedo tomar algo para matar ese virus?	Is there any kind of treatment? Can't I take something to kill the virus?
Gynecologist:	Yes, there is a treatment and it's called a LEEP. It's a surgical procedure, and I want your consent today so we can set it up.		
Patient:		¡¡¡Por supuesto!!! Lo que usted diga, lo que sea necesario. Yo autorizaré o firmaré lo que sea, para evitar el cáncer.	Of course!! Whatever you say. Whatever is necessary, I'll authorize or sign or whatever to avoid cancer.

Gynecologist:	Well I need to explain some things first. LEEP is a surgical procedure done under general anesthesia in the Same Day Surgery Unit of this hospital. So, in other words, in the building next store by the fountain.		
Patient:		Ah ya, sí sé dónde está.	Uh, yeah, I know right where it is.
Gynecologist:	LEEP means Loop Electrical Excision Procedure and I'll use an instrument shaped like a loop with electricity to remove the abnormal cells from your cervix.		
Patient:		Bueno, eso suena como que me va a doler. ¿Cierto?	Ok, but that sounds like it's going to hurt, doesn't it?
Gynecologist:	No, not really, you'll be under anesthesia. Our intention is to remove only the abnormal cells and leave as many as the healthy cells as possible.		
Patient:		Bueno. Usted es la que sabe y yo me pongo en sus manos.	Sure, you know what you're doing and I'm in your hands.
Gynecologist:	Do you plan on getting pregnant again?		
Patient:		No, yo ya tengo mis tres hijos. El último es todavía un bebé y con tres basta y sobra. Además, me operé y ahora estoy separada del infeliz de mi marido.	No, I have my three kids and the last one's still a baby. Three is more than enough. Besides, I had my tubes tied and I'm separated from the bastard that used to be my husband.
Gynecologist:	OK, because one of the risks is if we take out too much of the cervix during this procedure, it might be difficult to maintain a pregnancy in the future, because the uterus might not be as strong as it was before the procedure.		

Patient:		Entiendo eso, pero no me preocupa mucho, por que como le dije, tres chamacos son más que suficientes.	I understand that, but I'm not too worried, because like I said, three kids are enough.
Gynecologist:	That's one less risk to worry about, but there are some others I need to go over with you. As with any operation, there's the risk of infection. Since we're using an instrument, there's the possibility of damaging the vagina or other organs nearby; you could have heavy bleeding afterwards; and as I mentioned before, the cervix could become damaged or scarred.		
Patient:		Me asusta un poco, pero sé que estoy en buenas manos.	It's a little scary, but I know that I am in good hands.
Gynecologist:	There is also a risk that we will not get all of the abnormal cells and we'd have to repeat the LEEP.		
Patient:		Bueno.	OK.
Gynecologist:	All right, then. I reviewed how we got to this point, and what I'm proposing that we do and why I think we should do it. I also explained the procedure to you and what risks are involved. What are your questions?		
Patient:		No tengo ninguna pregunta. Todo me quedó muy claro. Estoy lista para hacerme esto y para salir adelante.	I don't have any questions. Everything is crystal clear. I'm ready to have this done and move on.
Gynecologist:	If you don't have any questions, please sign here, and print your name here. Then put the date, please.		

Patient:		(Patient signs). Oh, sí tengo una pregunta. Con los otros exámenes, como la endoscopía, los ultrasonidos, las tomografías, uno, el paciente tiene que llamar y programar la cita; para este examen, el… ¿Cómo se dice?, el…	Oh, I do have a question. With the other tests, like an endoscopy, an ultrasound, a CAT scan, you have to call and make your own appointment. For this one…the…what's it called?
Gynecologist:	The LEEP? No. The process is different. We have the signed consent now and I'm going to send that over with your other paperwork. They'll review the surgical schedule and then call you with a few dates. You can pick the date that is best for you.		
Patient:		¿Me van a ingresar en el hospital? ¿Cuánto tiempo voy a estar ahí?	Will I be admitted to the hospital? How long will I be there?
Gynecologist:	The procedure itself takes about 45 minutes and they ask you to be there about two hours early. Afterwards you need about an hour to get over the anesthesia, and then they discharge you. So I think about four hours or half a day.		
Patient:		Bueno. Tengo que buscar quién me cuide al bebé ese día.	OK. I'll have to find someone to watch the baby that day.
Gynecologist:	One more thing: if you don't hear anything from us in about two weeks, please call and let us know. This is something we have to take care of soon. Any last questions?		
Patient:		No, todo está muy claro. Gracias, Doctorcita.	No, everything is very clear. Thank you doctor.

Learning Objective 2.3

After completing this section and its corresponding exercises, the learner will be able to:
Objective 2.3(a)
- Describe three memory processes: encoding, storage and retrieval.
Objective 2.3(b)
- Practice three cognitive strategies: mnemonics, chunking and imagery.

 Learning Activity 2.3(a): Test Your Memory Skills!

Instructions (Part A)

- This activity is a competition!
- Your instructor will display a list of medical items on a screen.
- The list will be displayed for 60 seconds. Do not write anything.
- The list will disappear.
- Now write down as many items as you can remember.
- The person who lists the most items correctly wins this activity!

Now answer these questions.

1. Which items did you remember best: those at the beginning of the list? The middle? Or the end?

_____

_____

_____

2. Perhaps you are an exception, but most people remember items at the very beginning or end of a list. Why do you think they do so?

_____

_____

_____

Instructions (Part B)

- This activity is another competition!
- Your instructor will display a list of nonsense terms on a screen.
- The list will be displayed for 60 seconds. Do not write anything.
- The list will disappear.
- Now write down as many items as you can remember.
- The person who lists the most items correctly wins this activity!

Now answer these questions.

1. Which items did you remember best: those from the medical list or the nonsense list?

_____

_____

_____

2. Most people seem to remember items from the medical list better than those from the nonsense list. Why do you think they do?

_____

_____

_____

 Learning Activity 2.3(b): Memory Skills Practice

Instructions

- Work in pairs.
- Your instructor will hand you or display a picture (either a landscape such as a mountain or beach or, if preferred for medical interpreters, a hospital or medical setting).
- Each partner will take turns.
- For your turn, look at the picture for 10 seconds and try to remember all the details.
- Then close your eyes. In two minutes, tell a story as if *you* were in the picture *naming as many details from the picture as possible.*
- The instructor will then hand you or display another picture.
- The second partner will follow the same instructions.
- After each session, you can give the partner who had to tell the story concrete, concise and constructive (CCC) feedback about what the partner remembered well and what your partner might have missed.

 Learning Activity 2.3(c): Chunking

Instructions (Part A)

- Your instructor will display, for 10 seconds, a large sheet with 10 big letters written on it.
- The sheet will disappear.
- Write down as many of the letters as you remember.
- Some participants may remember all (or most) of the 10 letters.
- Discuss *how those participants were able to remember the 10 letters.*

Instructions (Part B)

- Your instructor will display, for 10 seconds, a large sheet with 10 big numbers written on it.
- The sheet will disappear.
- Write down as many of the numbers as you remember.
- Some participants may remember all (or most) of them.
- Discuss *how those participants were able to remember the 10 numbers.*

Learning Objective 2.4

After completing this section and its corresponding exercises, the learner will be able to:
Objective 2.4(a)
• Practice three cognitive processes: anticipating, multitasking and message analysis.
Objective 2.4(b)
• Explore two interpreting skills-building strategies: parroting (shadowing) and paraphrasing.

 Learning Activity 2.4(a): Anticipation

Instructions

• Work in pairs. Call one person A and the other person B.
• Each person will read out loud one of the texts below, either in this book or on a handout.
• Partner A *will not look at the book or handouts.*
• Partner B will read text #1 below and pause before every shaded term.
• Partner A *will try to guess what that term might be.*
• Partner B each time will say "yes" and write a checkmark above that term (if guessed correctly by A or if a reasonable substitute was made) or say "no" and write X above that term (if A did not guess correctly or suggest a reasonable substitute).
• After this exercise, Partner A will show Partner B the list showing what was guessed correctly or incorrectly.
• Now reverse roles and do the same exercise again, using Text #2.

Note: This exercise may be difficult for you, especially if English is not one of your working languages. Do not worry. If you correctly anticipate (guess) even half the words, that is an excellent score.

These texts have around 150 words in total and have 15 gaps.

1. Asthma[9] is a condition in which your airways narrow and swell and produce extra mucus. This can make breathing difficult and trigger coughing, wheezing and shortness of breath.
Asthma can't be cured, but its symptoms can be controlled. Because asthma often changes over time, it's important that you work with your doctor to track your signs and symptoms and adjust treatment as needed.
Asthma symptoms range from minor to severe and vary from person to person. You may have infrequent asthma attacks, have symptoms only at certain times or have symptoms all the time.
Asthma signs and symptoms include:
• Shortness of breath
• Chest tightness or pain
• Trouble sleeping caused by shortness of breath, coughing or wheezing
• A whistling or wheezing sound when exhaling (wheezing is a common sign of asthma in children)
• Coughing or wheezing attacks that are worsened by a respiratory virus, such as a cold or the flu

---

[9]http://www.mayoclinic.org/diseases-conditions/asthma/basics/symptoms/con-20026992

2. Hypertension[10] is a common condition in which the force of the blood against your artery walls is high enough that it may eventually cause health problems, such as heart disease.

Hypertension is determined by the amount of blood your heart pumps and the amount of resistance to blood flow in your arteries. The more blood your heart pumps and the narrower your arteries, the higher your blood pressure.

You can have high blood pressure for years without any symptoms. Even without symptoms, damage to blood vessels and your heart continues and can be detected. Uncontrolled high blood pressure increases your risk of serious health problems, including heart attack and stroke.

High blood pressure generally develops over many years, and it affects nearly everyone eventually. Fortunately, high blood pressure can be easily detected. And once you know you have high blood pressure, you can work with your doctor to control it.

 Learning Activity 2.4(b): The Community Interpreter's Checklist

Instructions

- Work in pairs.
- Look at the checklist that follows these instructions *by yourself.*
- First, check any boxes that identify activities that you do, or *can* do, now.
- Next, write the word "URGENT" beside any activities or skills *NOT* checked that you find very important for community interpreters to master right away.
- Next, write the word, "SOON" beside any activities or skills *NOT* checked that you want to master soon.
- Finally, write the word "GOAL" beside any activities or skills *NOT* checked that you want to master over the long term.
- When you and your partner have finished these instructions, share your lists. Discuss: What was the same on your partner's list? What was different? Why?
- Next, see if you want to change any of the comments on your list (such as switching from "SOON" to "URGENT").

 Learning Activity 2.4(c): Parroting (Shadowing)

Instructions (Part A)

- Work in pairs.
- Remember that parroting (also known as shadowing) means repeating, word for word, exactly what a speaker says while the speaker is still speaking: an extremely important practice activity for interpreters.
- Take turns reading a text below. (Medical interpreters should select the first text about shingles.)
- The person parroting *will not look at the text.*
- The person reading the text will speak at a natural but slightly slow pace for about two minutes.
- The person parroting will do so *while the speaker is speaking* (or signing).
- After two minutes, change roles so that the second partner can practice parroting with either text.
- Continue taking turns until your instructor ends the activity.
- Discuss with your partner how the parroting went. What was hard or easy? Why? How accurate were you? How long did it take before fatigue set in?

---

[10]http://www.mayoclinic.org/diseases-conditions/high-blood-pressure/basics/definition/con-20019580

THE COMMUNITY INTERPRETER'S CHECKLIST

Before the encounter
1. Get your pens, notepad and terminology resources ready. ☐
2. Analyze what the session is about to help you prepare and focus. ☐

At the beginning of the encounter
3. Scan the room to make a decision about which unobtrusive position to adopt. ☐
4. Smile and use body language to create rapport and show empathy. ☐
5. Use a calm, firm voice to help establish trust, credibility and professionalism. ☐
6. Give a professional introduction to establish clear parameters for the session. ☐
7. Listen to and analyze the service user's language and regionalisms. ☐
8. Discriminate other surrounding noise. ☐

While interpreting
9. Engage in active listening. ☐
10. Read body language (eye cues, hand gestures, leg positions, etc.). ☐
11. Use imagery to aid in retention. ☐
12. Replicate or take into account the speakers' tones, volumes and gestures. ☐
13. Reorganize and reformulate the message based on *meaning* (not the words). ☐
14. Remember to use direct speech (first person). ☐
15. Deliver the message in the target language in a clear, understandable voice. ☐
16. Become aware of, assess and do not act on your own biases. ☐
17. Avoid eye contact while interpreting. ☐
18. Take notes as needed; recognize and interpret from notes. ☐
19. Maintain objectivity, detachment and regard for safety. ☐
20. Maintain utmost accuracy. ☐
21. Engage in problem solving and decision making as needed. ☐
22. Switch to indirect speech (third person) if direct speech is problematic. ☐
23. Read body language and contextual cues (without making eye contact). ☐
24. Monitor your output. ☐
25. Intervene to correct yourself, if necessary. ☐
26. Manage turn taking. ☐
27. Maintain impartiality. ☐
28. Identify communication barriers. As needed, plan how to address them. ☐
29. Intervene only if the consequences of a miscommunication are serious. ☐
30. Switch back smoothly to interpreting after mediating. ☐
31. Maintain transparency: report even your own interventions. ☐
32. Avoid side conversations. ☐
33. Check a dictionary, glossary or other resource, if necessary. ☐
34. Switch modes as needed. ☐
35. Assess whether or not to perform a sight translation, if so requested. ☐
36. Change position as needed. ☐

After the session
37. Leave the room whenever the provider leaves. ☐
38. Avoid being alone with the service user, if possible. ☐
39. Debrief with the provider (if possible) if the session left an emotional impact. ☐
40. Practice self care strategies, as needed. ☐

Shingles[11]

Shingles is a disease caused by the varicella-zoster virus—the same virus that causes chickenpox. After you have chickenpox, the virus stays in your body. It may not cause problems for many years. As you get older, the virus may reappear as shingles. Although it is most common in people over age 50, anyone who has had chickenpox is at risk.

You can't catch shingles from someone who has it. However, if you have a shingles rash, you can pass the virus to someone who has never had chickenpox. This would usually be a child, who could get chickenpox instead of shingles. The virus spreads through direct contact with the rash, and cannot spread through the air.

Early signs of shingles include burning or shooting pain and tingling or itching, usually on one side of the body or face. The pain can be mild to severe. Rashes or blisters appear anywhere from one to 14 days later. If shingles appears on your face, it may affect your vision or hearing. The pain of shingles may last for weeks, months, or even years after the blisters have healed.

There is no cure for shingles. Early treatment with medicines that fight the virus may help. These medicines may also help prevent lingering pain.

A vaccine may prevent shingles or lessen its effects. The vaccine is recommended for people 60 or over. In some cases doctors may give it to people ages 50 to 59.

SNAP/Food Stamps[12]

Heat and Eat: State Responses to the Changed Federal Law

The SNAP/Food Stamp Program is the largest nutrition assistance program administered by the United States Department of Agriculture (USDA). The goal of the program is "to alleviate hunger and malnutrition … by increasing food purchasing power for all eligible households who apply for participation" as stated in the Food Stamp Act of 1977, as amended (P.L. 108-269). The program provides monthly benefits to eligible low-income families which can be used to purchase food. Through the electronic benefit transfer systems (EBT) the use of food stamp "coupons" is no longer the means in which a client receives their benefits. EBT replaces paper coupons through use of a benefits card, similar to a bank card. USDA reports that all 50 states, DC, and Puerto Rico are now using EBT systems.

The federal government pays 100 percent of SNAP/Food Stamp program benefits. Federal and State governments share administrative costs (with the federal government contributing nearly 50 percent).

Every 5 years, the SNAP/Food Stamp program is reauthorized by Congress as part of the Farm Bill. The reauthorization establishes who is eligible for SNAP/food Stamps and addresses program access, benefit levels, and other matters.

The U.S. Department of Agriculture through the Food and Nutrition Service continues to conduct

---

[11]http://www.nlm.nih.gov/medlineplus/shingles.html
[12]http://frac.org/federal-foodnutrition-programs/snapfood-stamps/

research and studies aimed at improving the program. By improving access to the program in addition to on-going outreach and education, the USDA hopes to increase participation rates for those who are eligible for the SNAP/Food Stamps, but are not receiving benefits.

As of Oct. 1, 2008, SNAP is the new name for the federal Food Stamp Program. It stands for the Supplemental Nutrition Assistance Program. USDA has more information on the name change, as well as a chart of state names (pdf) for the SNAP program.

Instructions (Part B)

- Work alone.
- Start with your most fluent language (often called your A language).
- Select a recorded speech, a radio speaker, a television program or any other recording—but a *slow and simple* speech (at first)—about 100-120 words per minute (wpm).[13]
- Remember that parroting (or shadowing means repeating, word for word, exactly what a speaker says.
- Parrot two minutes of the recording.
- When you are ready, try a slightly faster speech (130-150 wpm) of about two minutes in the same language.
- When you are ready, try an even faster speech (more than 160 wpm) of about two minutes in the same language.

Instructions (Part C)

- Work alone.
- Once you have completed the work above, do the same steps as Part B for your weaker language(s).

Note: When you start off, choose speeches that address your main interests and make sure they are *simple* speeches (generally avoid TED talks, politicians and economists). You may find it fun to select speeches about people you know and your own culture, topics you have studied or your favorite hobbies, sports and leisure activities. However, when you get ready for an interpreting assignment, select recordings related to that topic. Medical interpreters: try not to challenge yourself with complex medical terminology at first. The purpose of this exercise is not reinforcing terminology but working on interpreting component skills.

 Learning Activity 2.4(d): Paraphrasing

Instructions (Part A)

- Work in pairs.
- Remember that paraphrasing means saying the same thing in different words *in the same language,* another extremely important practice activity for interpreters.
- Take turns reading the texts below. (Medical interpreters should select the medical texts.)

---

[13]For this exercise, sign language interpreters may wish to consider using appropriately paced online videos of speeches in signed language.

- The person paraphrasing *will not look at the text.*
- The person reading the text will speak in a natural clear voice and pause.
- The person paraphrasing will immediately say the same term, phrase or idiom or sentences from the short paragraphs in other words.
- After two minutes, change roles so that the second partner can practice paraphrasing.
- Continue taking turns until your instructor ends the activity.
- Discuss with your partner how the paraphrasing went. What was hard or easy? Why? How accurate were you? How long did it take before fatigue set in?

Generic List

Absolute	Deep
Challenging	Defect
Shout	Defend
Abuse	Dream
Active	Wise
Adult	Adverse
Development	Alternative
Anger	

Human migration[14] *is the movement of people from one place in the world to another for the purpose of taking up permanent or semipermanent residence, usually across a political boundary. An example of "semipermanent residence" would be the seasonal movements of migrant farm laborers. People can either choose to move ("voluntary migration") or be forced to move ("involuntary migration").*
Migrations have occurred throughout human history, beginning with the movements of the first human groups from their origins in East Africa to their current location in the world.
Migration occurs at a variety of scales: intercontinental (between continents), intracontinental (between countries on a given continent), and interregional (within countries). One of the most significant migration patterns has been rural to urban migration.

Medical List

Diagnosis	Antiseptic
Abdomen	Operation
Chronic	Anxiety
Addiction	Excision
Disease	Atrophy
Lump	Pain
Forget	Dilate
Antidote	

---

[14]http://www.nationalgeographic.com/xpeditions/lessons/09/g68/migrationguidestudent.pdf

Well-being and health promotion[15]

Health is more than the absence of disease; it is a resource that allows people to realize their aspirations, satisfy their needs and to cope with the environment in order to live a long, productive, and fruitful life. In this sense, health enables social, economic and personal development fundamental to well-being. Health promotion is the process of enabling people to increase control over, and to improve their health. Environmental and social resources for health can include: peace, economic security, a stable ecosystem, and safe housing. Individual resources for health can include: physical activity, healthful diet, social ties, resiliency, positive emotions, and autonomy. Health promotion activities aimed at strengthening such individual, environmental and social resources may ultimately improve well-being.

Instructions (Part B)

- Work alone.
- Start with your most fluent language (often called your A language).
- Select a recorded speech, a radio speaker, a television program or any other recording—but a *slow and simple* speech (at first)—about 100-120 wpm.
- Restate the sentences in the same language, keeping the same meaning.
- Paraphrase about two minutes recording—while the speaker is speaking if possible.
- When you are ready, try a slightly faster speech (130-150 wpm) of about two minutes in the same language.
- When you are ready, try an even faster speech (more than 160 wpm) of about two minutes in the same language.

Instructions (Part C)

- Work alone.
- Once you have completed the work above, do the same steps as Part B for your weaker language(s).

---

[15]http://www.cdc.gov/hrqol/wellbeing.htm

Learning Objective 2.5

After completing this section and its corresponding exercises, the learner will be able to:
Objective 2.5(a)
- Engage in three modes of interpreting: consecutive, simultaneous and sight translation.

Objective 2.5(b)
- Understand the rationale, skills and requirements for summarization.

Objective 2.5(c)
- Define, describe and practice mode-switching.

 Learning Activity 2.5(a): Practice in Consecutive Interpreting

Instructions

The instructor will divide the class into groups of three who speak the same language, if possible. One participant will play the interpreter, another will act as the doctor and the other will act as the patient.

The interpreter *must close this workbook now and MUST NOT look at the text while acting as the interpreter.*

If only two same-language role players are available, one person will read out the text of both the patient and the doctor.

Where possible, let the person playing the patient (or provider) read the text out loud in another working language of the interpreter (this is sight translation, but it need not be accurate). Doing so will allow the interpreter to practice going back and forth between two languages (bidirectional interpreting).

Otherwise, both doctor and patient will speak in English and the interpreter will interpret the entire dialogue into his or her other working language.

The interpreter will interpret everything stated in consecutive mode. *Sign language interpreters may work in simultaneous mode depending on the instructor's directions.*

After each role play, let someone else play the interpreter.

Remember, always, *that the person playing the interpreter must close this workbook and not try to look at the text.*

Medical role play for consecutive practice: The hand rash

First-year resident, internal medicine:	Good morning, Miss Peralta, I'm Dr. Hazari. I know you usually see Dr. Palyca, but because this is an emergency appointment, I'll be seeing you today. Tell me, what is going on?		
Patient:		Tengo esta alergia bien fea en la mano derecha y me duele mucho. Se me ha partido la piel todo por aquí—mire (patient points to her hand).	I have a really nasty rash on my right hand and it hurts. The skin is all cracked open here—look (patient points to her hand).
First-year resident, internal medicine:	(With back to the patient, typing on the computer) When did you first notice it? Oh, by the way, I am going to put your information in the computer while we talk, since it's late and you were added on to my schedule. So, when did you first notice it?		
Patient:		Amanecí así el miércoles, no, miento, el martes—sí, el martes fue, después de que me cambiaron de funciones en el trabajo.	I woke up on Wednesday, no, I'm wrong, on Tuesday—yeah, it was Tuesday, after they changed my duties at work.
First-year resident, internal medicine:	What do you do? Where do you work?		
Patient:		Trabajo en limpieza, pero no de casas, sino de edificios, oficinas, negocios; esa clase de limpieza, o sea profesional.	I work in cleaning, but I don't do houses, I clean offices, buildings, businesses, that is the kind of cleaning I do, I mean professional cleaning.

First-year resident, internal medicine:	Were you doing that kind of cleaning before, because you said that they changed your duties, right? How did they change?		
Patient:		Sí, antes yo sacaba la basura, pero ahora, me han puesto a limpiar los baños con químicos—son fuertes y cuando estoy limpiando me salpican por todas partes. El martes se me regó todo encima de la mano y el miércoles me desperté con esto.	Yeah, I used to take out the trash, but now, they have me cleaning the bathrooms using chemicals—they are strong and when I'm cleaning, they splatter all over. On Tuesday they spilled all over my hand and Wednesday I woke up like this.
First-year resident, internal medicine:	Well what spilled all over your hands? Was it bleacher, ammonia, cleanser, disinfectant?		
Patient:		Ah, yo no sé, disculpe, creo que sí. Las botellas no tienen etiquetas, pero huelen a cloro.	Oh, I don't know, I'm sorry, I think so. The bottles don't have labels, but they smell like bleach.
First-year resident, internal medicine:	So, Tuesday you were at work and an irritating chemical irritant spilled on your hands; you woke up Wednesday with contact dermatitis. Today is Friday, so it's been— Wednesday, Thursday, Friday—three days. Is that correct? (typing)		
Patient:		Uh…no, lo que haya sido me dio una alergia del madres.	Uh…no, whatever it was, it really gave me a rash.
First-year resident, internal medicine:	Yes, that is what I said. OK—about the rash: did it start in one place and spread around, or was it like that from the beginning?		

Patient:		Cuando me desperté, ya estaba así.	When I woke up, it was already like that.
First-year resident, internal medicine:	Does it itch or hurt?		
Patient:		Sí, me arde come bastante y me duele, no aguanto más.	Yes, it really itches and it hurts. I can't stand it anymore.
First-year resident, internal medicine:	Did you get any vesicles, ulcerations, blisters or redness, or is the rash scaly?		
Patient:		Sí, está rojo y tengo granitos que se enconan.	Yes, it's red and I have blisters that are getting infected.
First-year resident, internal medicine:	Do they ooze?		
Patient:		Más o menos, sí me sale pus.	More or less, yes there's pus that comes out.
First-year resident, internal medicine:	Did you have a fever, joint pain or an upper respiratory infection lately, or in the last three days?		
Patient:		No.	No.
First-year resident, internal medicine:	Do you have a history of any skin diseases or any other health problems?		
Patient:		No.	No.
First-year resident, internal medicine:	Do you or anyone in your family have a history of allergies, asthma or eczema?		
Patient:		Unos familiares sufren de alergia al polen de los árboles, algo así, y creo que tengo un sobrino en Santo Domingo al que recién le dio asma. Además de eso, no sé.	I have some relatives with allergies, from trees or something like that, and I think I have a nephew who has asthma. Apart from that, I don't know.

First-year resident, internal medicine:	Did you fall or have any trauma to your hand in the last three days?		
Patient:		No, que yo me acuerde, no.	No, not that I remember, no.
First-year resident, internal medicine:	Ok—contact dermatitis, with purulent vesicles, erythema, pruritus, three days. (typing)		
Patient:		¿Sí?	What?
First-year resident, internal medicine:	Have you taken anything for it?		
Patient:		No todavía, no. Deme una pomada o algo, porque tengo que volver a trabajar mañana.	Not yet, no. Can you give me an ointment or something? Because I have to go back to work tomorrow.
First-year resident, internal medicine:	I am. I'm going to give you a cream to put on your hand and that should help. The redness should go away in about a week and the vesicles, or the blisters will drain and get crusty, but they will dry up in a few days.		
Patient:		Gracias, doctor.	Thank you, doctor.
First-year resident, internal medicine:	The way you can prevent this from happening again is to keep those chemicals off your skin. I suggest wearing gloves, and if the chemicals do get on your skin, wash them off with soap and water right away. Is there anything else today?		

Patient:		Pues, sí. Antes, cuando pasaba el trapeador—porque me tocaba hacerlo tres noches a la semana, me dolía aquí en la cintura (puts hand on waist). También cuando me estiraba para limpiar encima de los estantes, me daban dolores aquí en el brazo y por aquí en el hombro (runs hand up the arm to the shoulder). No hacía caso a estos dolores antes, pero ahora que estoy aquí, le digo.	Well, yes. When I used to mop before—because it was the job I used to do three nights a week, my lower back hurt (puts hand on waist). And, when I used to stretch to clean on top of the shelves, it hurt here in my shoulder and in my arm (runs hand up the arm to the shoulder). I didn't pay much attention to the pain before, but since I am here, I'm just mentioning it.
First-year resident, internal medicine:	Oh, we'll have to talk about that at your next visit, or you can talk to Dr. Palyca about it, since he's your PCP. Remember this was just an emergency appointment. You can try ibuprofen in the meantime.		
Patient:		Ah, bueno. Gracias. ¿Eso es todo?	Oh, OK. Thanks. Is that it?
First-year resident, internal medicine:	Yes.		

Human services role play for consecutive practice: Transportation passes (English-Spanish)[16]

Provider:	Our officials have decided to issue special identification passes to some students that could restrict their use of subsidized public transportation.		
Client:		¿Puede explicar que es el transporte subsidiado?	Can you please explain what subsidized transportation is?
Provider:	Up until now, students could use public transportation for half the cost by using their school ID. But with the increase we're seeing in young people running in groups taking advantage of people, we feel we need to implement a special identification system. The new ID card will identify the students by name and school.		
Client:		No creo que esto funcione, los alumnos pueden perder o intercambiar su identificación.	I don't think this will work; students can lose or trade their ID.
Provider:	The new system will have a chip in the ID and can restrict travel after 8 PM.		
Client:		¿Entonces, esto quiere decir que mi hija no puede ir a trabajar después de las 8:00? Ella sale de trabajar a las 9:30 PM. ¿Que se supone que hagamos? ¿Sugiere algo?	So this means that my daughter can't go to work after 8 p.m.? She gets off at 9:30 p.m. What are we supposed to do? Do you have suggestions?

16Adapted from Bancroft and Rubio-Fitzpatrick (2011), *The Community Interpreter: A Comprehensive Training Manual*, 5th ed. Columbia, MD: Culture & Language Press, pp. pp. 128-129.

Provider:	The problem is that our city has become unsafe because of the number of youth stealing phones and devices from bus and metro riders.		
Client:		No todos los jóvenes están metidos en esas cosas, ¿por qué castigar a los chicos trabajadores?	Not all young people are involved in that stuff. Why do you punish the kids who are hard working?
Provider:	Remember that the city has curfew for anyone under 17 years old and it's different depending on the time of the year and day.		
Client:		Lo sé pero dependemos del sueldo de mi hija para salir adelante. ¿Qué podemos hacer?	I know but we depend on my daughter's salary to get ahead. What can we do?
Provider:	There are some options. If your daughter works that late, it means she is older than 17 so the ID won't allow her to use subsidized travel but she can pay full price and still travel. You can also make arrangements to pick her up.		
Client:		Este plan no me gusta, pero puede que ayude a tener una ciudad más segura.	I don't like this plan but it might help to have a safer city.

Medical role plays for consecutive practice: Just for fun!
(English only)

Excerpt: House MD TV Episode, script 105, "Paternity"[17]

Doctor:	So, you have family here in Princeton?	
Patient:		No.
Doctor:	Here on work?	
Patient:		No.
Doctor:	Why are you…? Does your penis hurt?	
Patient:		No… What? Should it?
Doctor:	No. Just thought I'd toss you a really inappropriate question. Your lawyer's gonna love it.	
Patient:		Why would I want to sue you? I want you to treat me.
Doctor:	You're from New Brunswick, New Jersey, right?	
Patient:		Yeah.
Doctor:	Now, why would you drive 70 miles to get treatment for a condition that a nine-year-old could diagnose? It's the free-flowing pus that's the tip-off.	
Patient:		I was in town.
Doctor:	Not for family. Not for work…	
Patient:		That's right!
Doctor:	You drove 70 miles to a walk-in clinic. You passed two hospitals on the road. Either you've got a problem with those hospitals, or they have a problem with you. My guess is you've sued half the doctors in Maplewood, and the rest are now refusing to help you.	
Patient:		It's ironic, isn't it? Sort of like the boy who sued wolf.

[17]http://www.springfieldspringfield.co.uk/view_episode_scripts.php?tv-show=house-md&episode=s01e02

Doctor:	You know? I bet we have a doctor here named Wolf. How perfect would that be? - I'm gonna page him…	
Patient:		Okay. You know what? Thank you. I'm gonna find a doctor to take care of this.
Doctor:	I didn't say I wouldn't treat you. - We'll drain your knee, run some lab work. Fix you up.	
Patient:		Why would you do that? I'm a people person.

Excerpt: House MD TV episode, script 107 "Fidelity"[18]

Doctor:	Anything else besides the shortness of breath?	
Patient:		Not really. It's actually just kind of a tightness.
Doctor:	You smoke?	
Patient		No, never. […]
Doctor:	Any history of heart disease in your family?	
Patient:		Not that I know of.
Doctor:	Take a deep breath. Been under a lot of stress lately?	
Patient:		No more than usual.
Doctor:	You're probably just a little anemic. I'm gonna do an E.K.G. Just to make sure.	
Patient:		Do I need to take this off?
Doctor:	Uh, no. You can just pull that down in front. Good Lord. Are those real?	
Patient:		Do they look real?
Doctor:	They look pretty damn good.	
Patient:		They were a present for my husband's 40th. I figured he'd enjoy them more than a sweater.

---

[18]http://www.springfieldspringfield.co.uk/view_episode_scripts.php?tv-show=house-md&episode=s01e07

Doctor:	That's so sweet. But I'm afraid the cause of your problem could be staring us right in the face.	
Patient:		Staring us…?
Doctor:	Actually, I guess I'm the one doing the staring. Of course, I can't be sure. I'd like to consult a colleague. He's actually somewhat of an expert in these matters.	
	[…]	
Doctor:	Try to remain as still as possible. The less distortion there is, the more detail we'll be able to see.	
Patient:		Okay. Ow!
Doctor:	I'm sorry. I know it's uncomfortable. The tighter we go, the better the image will be.	
Patient:		At least it'll keep me awake.
Doctor:	Don't worry. It's almost over.	
Patient:		I wish people would stop telling me not to worry.
Doctor:	I'm sorry.	

Learning Activity 2.5(b): "I Need Another Interpreter": Educating the Requester

Instructions

- Select one of the situations below. **Medical interpreters should select Scenario C.**
- Each of these scenarios involves an interpreter being asked to perform *simultaneous* interpreting alone for more than two hours.
- Let us say, or pretend, that you are already skilled enough in simultaneous interpreting to accept the assignment.
- Your job is to educate the requester that you will need a "team interpreter"—someone who will interpret with you so that you can "trade off" every 15–30 minutes as needed.

  Remember: No interpreter should perform simultaneous interpreting alone for longer than 45 minutes because the interpreter's performance will then be dangerously inaccurate.

- Decide: what will you tell the requester? You want the assignment, but only if they will provide another interpreter who is skilled in simultaneous. (**Hint**: Remember the **SAY NO** model!)
- Write your answer in the blank lines provided following the scenarios.

Scenario A: Education

You have been asked to interpret at a school for a two-hour parent teacher association meeting. You will be interpreting in simultaneous mode for various persons who are making speeches and presentations on important topics. The school system will provide equipment but you have been asked to interpret alone.

Scenario B: Community meeting

You have been asked to interpret for a two-hour public meeting between candidates for a municipal election who are giving speeches and engaging in a public debate. The interpreting will be simultaneous. The group that has engaged you to interpret expects you to perform alone.

Scenario C: Health education

You have been asked to interpret for a two-hour seminar at the local hospital on smoking cessation (how to quit smoking). Except for any questions and answers, the entire evening will involve simultaneous interpreting and you are expected to perform alone.

What will you say to the requester?

_____

_____

_____

_____

_____

_____

Learning Activity 2.5(c): Practice in Simultaneous Interpreting

Instructions

- Select any of the texts below. Medical interpreters should select the medical texts.
- In pairs, take turns having one person read the text out loud while the other person interprets it in simultaneous mode.

Text A   Education: Speech therapy

Knowing your child needs speech therapy is important. The earlier you get help for your child, the better the chance your child will speak like any other kid. But what exactly are speech and language disorders?

Well, a speech disorder refers to problems actually producing sounds. Language disorders are a bit different because they relate to any difficulty someone might have understanding words or putting them together to communicate ideas.

There are quite a number of speech disorders around. Articulation disorders involve difficulty producing sounds in syllables that people can understand. A fluency disorder like stuttering interrupts the speech flow with some kind of stoppages, like repetitions or stretching out sounds and syllables. Voice disorders mean having trouble with pitch or volume or voice quality, which interferes with people understanding what you say.

Language disorders, on the other hand, tend to be receptive or expressive. Receptive disorders refer to the kind of problems people have understanding language or processing it. They're different from expressive orders, where the trouble comes trying to put words together into coherent chunks of meaning that people can understand and follow.

But whether your child has a speech disorder or a language disorder, specialists in speech language therapy offer a host of services that will make all the difference.

Text B   Healthcare: Ulcerative Colitis

All of you here today have ulcerative colitis. We understand the diagnosis may seem overwhelming at first, but even now that you are used to it and being treated, it probably still raises a lot of questions in your mind, and that's what we're going to talk about with you right now. We'll start with what exactly ulcerative colitis is, how it affects your life and whether you'll always have to deal with it. First, though, I want to start off by sharing with you that I have it myself, so I know what it's like.

I know how worried you probably felt when you got the news and how you want to learn as much about it as you can, so you can work with your doctor to build a treatment plan that makes sense to you and allows you to live a healthy and happy life. I also know what it's like to worry when a flareup comes when you least expect it and what it feels like to be afraid you might lose your colon.

90

You already know that ulcerative colitis, or UC, like Crohn's disease, is an inflammatory bowel disease, or IBD. What you might not be aware of is that IBD affects more than 1.4 million Americans. Quite a lot! Even if it sounds large, it does mean not every general practitioner or primary care physician is going to have the kind of experience to treat it in the best way possible, so the first question to consider is whether you have a gastroenterologist. That's the kind of doctor who specializes in treating conditions that affect the digestive tract, so that's where you start. You want a doctor with lots of experience treating UC.

Text C   Social Services: Child Support—Establishing Paternity[19]

Paternity establishment is important! Your child deserves all of the advantages in life that two parents can give. There are some special reasons to establish paternity.

First, there may be benefits for your child. Your child may be eligible for some benefits because you have established paternity. These benefits may include Social Security, veteran's benefits, health insurance, life insurance and inheritance. Establishing paternity ensures you can provide for your child even when the unexpected occurs.

Second, you will have more information for your child's medical history. Knowing the family's full history of diseases, illnesses and birth defects will help your doctor if your child becomes sick. It's important to know the father's medical history for this reason.

Finally, there is the question of child support. Your child needs and deserves both emotional and financial support from both parents. You may think that you can get by on your own and live without any help from your child's father. But you may change your mind some day. A court can't order child support without legal proof of paternity. It's easier to get that proof today than to wait.

Text D   Fine-Needle Biopsies[20]

Fine-needle aspiration is a type of biopsy procedure. In fine-needle aspiration, a thin needle is inserted into an area of abnormal-appearing tissue or body fluid.

As with other types of biopsies, the sample collected during fine-needle aspiration can help make a diagnosis or rule out conditions such as cancer. Fine-needle aspiration is generally considered a safe procedure. Complications are infrequent.

A fine-needle aspiration is most often done on swellings or lumps located just under the skin. A lump may be felt during a doctor's examination. Or it may be discovered on an imaging test such as:

> CT scan
> mammogram
> ultrasound

---

[19]Slightly adapted from Maryland Department of Human Resources, http://www.dhr.state.md.us/blog/?page_id=10276
[20]http://www.webmd.com/a-to-z-guides/fine-needle-aspiration

Imaging tests may also discover abnormal spots deeper inside the body. Doctors may recommend fine-needle aspiration for areas such as:

> cysts (fluid-filled lumps)
> nodules or masses (solid lumps)
> enlarged lymph nodes

Without a biopsy, it's usually hard for a doctor to confirm what these abnormal areas contain. And you may not know if they are a threat to your health.

The most common reason to get a fine-needle aspiration is to test for cancer. Most fine-needle aspirations are done on these areas:

> breast
> thyroid gland
> lymph nodes in the neck, groin, or armpit

Those types of fine needle aspirations are performed through the skin.

Using endoscopy, doctors can also reach areas deeper in the body. An endoscopy uses a flexible tube with a light and camera attached. During an endoscopy, a doctor can do a fine-needle aspiration on certain abnormal spots in the chest or abdomen.

There is no one standard preparation before fine-needle aspiration. You may be asked to take these preparations:

Changes in medicines. Several days before the test, stop taking aspirin or other blood thinners. These include Plavix (clopidogrel) or brand-name versions of the generic drug warfarin. The brand names of warfarin are:

> Coumadin
> Jantoven

Changes in diet. Do not eat or drink anything for several hours before the procedure.
If you will be getting sedating medication, be sure to bring someone with you to drive you home.

 Learning Activity 2.5(d): Practice in Whisper Interpreting (Chuchotage)

Instructions

- Follow the instructions above.
- However, the interpreter should be positioned near the service user/patient and interpret close to that person's ear.
- Whoever plays the interpreter *should speak in a low voice but must not whisper.* (Remember that whispering is bad for one's voice and can, over time, can actually damage the vocal cords.)
- After finishing as many role plays as time permits, discuss in your group what you felt the differences were for you between *simultaneous* interpreting (in the previous exercise) and *whisper* interpreting (also known as whispered simultaneous or *chuchotage*).

Instructions

- Work in pairs.
- Select one of the texts below. Medical interpreters should select Text A, B or D.
- Read and prepare to sight translate the text and mark it up as needed or desired.
- When you are ready, take turns sight translating the text to your partner.
- As you listen to your partner, read the text and note what went well and what was omitted by marking up that portion of the text.
- After completing the exercise, if time permits give feedback to your partner.
- Remember to start with positive feedback and then make concrete, concise and constructive (CCC) suggestions.

Text A   Breast Cancer[21]

Breast cancer affects one in eight women during their lives. Breast cancer kills more women in the United States than any cancer except lung cancer. No one knows why some women get breast cancer, but there are a number of risk factors. Risks that you cannot change include
Age—the chance of getting breast cancer rises as a woman gets older.
Genes—there are two genes, BRCA1 and BRCA2, that greatly increase the risk. Women who have family members with breast or ovarian cancer may wish to be tested.
Personal factors—beginning periods before age 12 or going through menopause after age 55.

Other risks include being overweight, using hormone replacement therapy (also called menopausal hormone therapy), taking birth control pills, drinking alcohol, not having children or having your first child after age 35 or having dense breasts.

Symptoms of breast cancer may include a lump in the breast, a change in size or shape of the breast or discharge from a nipple. Breast self-exam and mammography can help find breast cancer early when it is most treatable. Treatment may consist of radiation, lumpectomy, mastectomy, chemotherapy and hormone therapy.

Men can have breast cancer, too, but the number of cases is small.

Text B   The Prostate Gland[22]

The prostate is the gland below a man's bladder that produces fluid for semen. Prostate cancer is common among older men. It is rare in men younger than 40. Risk factors for developing prostate cancer include being over 65 years of age, family history, and being African-American.

---

[21]http://www.nlm.nih.gov/medlineplus/breastcancer.html
[22]http://www.nlm.nih.gov/medlineplus/prostatecancer.html

Symptoms of prostate cancer may include
- *Problems passing urine, such as pain, difficulty starting or stopping the stream, or dribbling*
- *Low back pain*
- *Pain with ejaculation*

To diagnose prostate cancer, your doctor may do a digital rectal exam to feel the prostate for lumps or anything unusual. You may also get a blood test. These tests are also used in prostate cancer screening, which looks for cancer before you have symptoms. If your results are abnormal, you may need more tests, such as an ultrasound, MRI, or biopsy.

Treatment often depends on the stage of the cancer. How fast the cancer grows and how different it is from surrounding tissue helps determine the stage. Men with prostate cancer have many treatment options. The treatment that's best for one man may not be best for another. The options include watchful waiting, surgery, radiation therapy, hormone therapy, and chemotherapy. You may have a combination of treatments.

Text C   Student intervention teams (SIT) procedures[23]

The Student Intervention Team process consists of consultation and problem solving, which focuses on the needs of an individual student. The identified student, in spite of having received the benefit of evidence-based tier 1 and tier 2 instruction or interventions, has not shown the expected academic or behavioral growth. Consultation with the school Student Intervention Team is needed to explore more intensive and individualized intervention options. The Student Intervention Team is composed of knowledgeable school staff and the student's family, who work collaboratively to: (1) deeply examine student strength and needs, (2) to analyze the student's response to previous interventions, (3) and use a root-cause analysis approach to develop a systematic plan for intensive interventions, which are designed to close the academic or behavioral gap between the student and his or her peers. The team uses a continuous problem-solving process to review and revise plans as needed until the student achieves goals.

Student Intervention Team Process
- *The referring teacher completes and submits the initial referral form to the SIT chairperson. A designated consultant (DC) is assigned.*
- *The referring teacher consults with the DC to complete the Student Intervention Team Body of Evidence forms, gather supporting data, and refine the problem definition in preparation for the SIT meeting.*
- *Conduct the Student Intervention Team meeting...Create an intervention and progress monitoring plan.*
- *The DC and referring teacher meet to examine student progress monitoring data and analyze student response to instruction.*
- *Conduct follow-up SIT meeting six to nine weeks from the initial SIT meeting.*
- *Conduct consequent follow-up meetings as needed.*

---

[23]http://denver.co.schoolwebpages.com/education/components/scrapbook/default.php?sectiondetailid=1145

Text D   Work Hardening and Work Conditioning[24]

When injured workers meet established short- and long-term goals via physical therapy or hand/occupational therapy but are unable to return to work due to remaining functional deficits or deconditioning, they may benefit from a higher level of therapeutic intervention designed specifically with a primary goal of returning to work. Injured workers who benefit most from these programs are usually at least 30 days out from their injury and have a medium or higher physical demand category job to return to. These are full body intensive conditioning programs that focus on work simulation activities to get injured workers back to work.

Work Hardening

A highly structured, goal-oriented, individualized intervention program designed to return the employee to work. Our Work Hardening programs are multidisciplinary in nature and utilize real or simulated work activities designed to restore physical, behavioral and vocational functions. Work Hardening addresses the issues of productivity, safety, physical tolerances and worker behaviors.

Work Conditioning

An intensive, goal-oriented conditioning program designed to restore neuromuscular and musculoskeletal function including strength, power, endurance, joint mobility, ROM, motor control, cardiovascular endurance and functional abilities. The primary objective of the Work Conditioning program is to restore physical capacity and function to enable the injured worker to return to his or her pre-injury job.

 Learning Activity 2.5(f): Practice in Summarization

Instructions

- Work in pairs.
- One person will read the text below (all speakers) out loud while the other partner listens.
- This text is a script for a medical emergency: the speakers are paramedics and family members frantically looking for a daughter who is buried in debris after an explosion inside a house.
- The reading partner will read it *very quickly—too quickly to interpret.*
- The listening partner will then try to interpret but ultimately summarize what was heard instead of interpreting.
- Let the reading partner give concrete, concise and constructive (CCC) feedback on the summarization.
- If time permits, change roles and do the same exercise again.

Excerpted from: ER Episode script "Fevers of Unknown Origin"[25]

---

[24]http://www.novacare.com/services/work-health/work-hardening-and-work-conditioning/
[25]http://www.springfieldspringfield.co.uk/view_episode_scripts.php?tv-show=er&episode=s02e20

Emergency Text (Part A)

Speaker 2: (L2) Becky girl! She's down here somewhere! It just blew up!

Speaker 1: Water heater was here? Your daughter's bed was there? Oh, my God! Please, sir! Please, you have to step away. You shouldn't be down here with bare feet! Please!

Speaker 2: It's my daughter!

Speaker 1: That's still standing water!

Speaker 3: I told you we needed a new one!

Speaker 1: We couldn't afford it.

Speaker 3: But we can afford bourbon every week!

Speaker 2: What..?

Speaker 1: Would you just shut up?

Speaker 2: What..?

Speaker 3: Reilly, go get backup.

Speaker 4: I got it.

Speaker 1: We're so weak.

Speaker 2: What..?

Speaker 3: I told you!

Speaker 1: Why don't you shut up! Look, all right, listen, just take it easy!

Speaker 4: What color pajamas is she wearing?

Speaker 2: (L2) What? Pink, I think…

Speaker 4: Look for the color. When was the explosion?

Speaker 2: (L2) What? I don't know. I think… Maybe… It was like 10 minutes ago.

Speaker 4: Backup's on the way!

Speaker 3: I found a foot!

Speaker 2: What..?

Speaker 1: All right! Yeah, here!

Speaker 2: (L2) All right, take it easy!

Speaker 4: There she is!

Speaker 2: (L2) Oh, my God! Becky girl! Oh, my God…!

Emergency Text (Part B)

Speaker 1: Not too close, not too close! Easy! Find her head! Gently! All right, let's go!

Speaker 3: Gently, all right? Let's roll her, get the board.

Speaker 4: Right.

Speaker 3: Oh, God! Weak pulse.

Speaker 2: What..?

Speaker 1: Breath sounds? Oh, my God! She's not breathing!

Speaker 2: What..?

Speaker 3: Reilly, get an ET tube! You with us?

Speaker 4: Yeah! Yeah! Come on, come on! Come on!

Speaker 1: Shoot!

Speaker 3: For crying out loud!

Speaker 4: I got another one!

Speaker 1: Come on! Here, here! She's got it.

Speaker 2: (L2) Thank God! Oh, Lord!

Speaker 1: Good breath sounds bilaterally.

Speaker 2: What..?

Speaker 3: Okay, darling, you're gonna be just fine. Let's wrap her up.

Speaker 1: Let's get her up.

Speaker 2: Come on, Becky, come on, Baby! You're gonna be fine! We'll take care of you!

Emergency Text (Part C)

I'm so sorry, I can't calm down. It must have been my entire fault. She had already told me that that chimney wasn't working ok. It was leaking for more than… Yes ok, I know! I gotta answer your question… I think she was sleeping… Or maybe playing, Becky has always been a stubborn kid. Becky wouldn't even respect her own mother. My wife and I were already sound asleep. At least, I think she was. I had returned late from work and my wife went to bed as soon as I arrived home. Becky must have been awake cause I saw her bedroom light on and heard some voice sounds… She's always talking with her invisible friend. Silly little brat! Her bed wasn't even close to the chimney. No ways. Yes, you're right. I know it was just found next to it, but I'm telling you it wasn't. I don't know how it ended up so close. You find it out. That's your job. Why are you accusing me? She was much worse than her mother. You gave her a hundred bucks she wanted two hundred. You bought her a pound of cookies, she wanted three ponds… I just heard two strong explosions. Don't ask me what. I have no idea. She must have had a balloon or something, cause the first explosion was louder… No, wait, the second was louder. I ordered my wife to get out of the house through the window and ran to save Becky… Oh, my poor little girl. Please, God, save her. She's suffered so much after her mother left us and now she's in that hospital bed all burnt and her little body all wrapped up in… Oh God, please…! Oh, yes. What was your third question again…?

 Learning Activity 2.5(g): Practice in Mode Switching

Instructions

- Work in groups of three following the usual instructions for role plays.
- However, these role plays will involve the interpreter needing to switch between consecutive, simultaneous and sight translation modes, in part because those playing the doctor and patient will speak *very quickly* at times.
- Role Play A involves the patient's daughter, but since the daughter never speaks, simply pretend that she is there but do not assign anyone to play that role (unless your group has four people).
- There are several places in the first role play where the interpreter has to switch modes, between consecutive and sight translation, or consecutive and simultaneous (or to summarize, if you don't yet feel able to perform simultaneous interpreting).
- The interpreter should stay alert.
- After each role play ends, if time permits discuss whether everyone agrees with how and when the interpreter switched modes.
- If appropriate, let the other two partners offer the interpreter concrete, concise and constructive (CCC) feedback.
- In Role Play A, switch interpreters where it instructs you to do so in the role play.

Mode-switching role play A: Glaucoma and eye drops (English-English only)

(Mrs. Markus has come to see to Dr. Bello's for the second time to get the official results of tests done on an eye infection. She is accompanied by her daughter, Monica.)

Dr. Bello:	Good morning Mrs. Markus and Monica, it's nice to see you again. Mrs. Markus, how is your right eye doing?	
Mrs. Markus:		Hi Dr. Bello, my eyes are feeling much better. The drops and ointment really worked.
Dr. Bello:	I'm really glad to hear that. I called you in today to discuss the results of the tests we did when we dilated your eyes. I'm afraid your tests did show a second issue with your eyes.	
Mrs. Markus:		Oh no. I was afraid of that! Both my grandfather and my aunt have glaucoma. Is that what you've found?
Dr. Bello:	Actually, yes. It turns out that the infection you had was unrelated to what we found. But you're very lucky that you did come in for treatment for the infection. You have what we call primary open-angled glaucoma. It's the most common type of glaucoma and you can it for years without realizing it.	
Mrs. Markus: *(turns to her daughter, Monica, and starts speaking rapidly. Wait to see how the interpreter handles it—hopefully he or she will switch to simultaneous or will summarize the side conversation)*		Oh my god. Glaucoma? I was afraid that's what he was going to say but somehow I didn't really think it would happen. What am I going to do? I can't go blind? How would I do anything? I won't be able to read or cook or drive! And how will I take care of your grandmother? She needs me more and more. I'm not the one whose supposed to be getting sick! I'm not sure I can handle this!
Dr. Bello: *(after listening to the simultaneous interpreting or the summarization)*	Mrs. Markus, I know it can be very scary to hear a diagnosis like this. But we caught the disease very early on.	

Mrs. Markus:		Early? What does that mean? Can you cure it?
Dr. Bello:	There is a very good chance we will be able to treat it so that you don't notice any worsening of your eyesight. If you hadn't come in for the other infection, we might not have caught it so early.	
	SWITCH INTERPRETER	
Mrs. Markus: (*starting to calm down*)		Okay. It just sounds so scary. I don't want to go blind! What kind of treatment do I have to go through?
Dr. Bello:	One of the ways glaucoma affects the eyes is by putting too much pressure on the optic lens. The first thing we do is give you daily eye drops that help to keep your eye pressure low.	
Mrs. Markus:		Drops? I hate drops. I can never get them in the right way.
Dr. Bello:	Don't worry. The nurse will teach you how to do that in just a minute.	
Mrs. Markus:		Oh that's good. Thank you.
Dr. Bello:	Now, the second thing we have to do is take care of any blockage or clogging in the eye. We will have to run a few more tests to see if you have blockage. If you do, then there are laser surgery treatments that are very effective.	
Mrs. Markus:		Okay. Well, I guess that doesn't sound too bad. I don't like putting drops in my eyes. It always stings and makes a mess. But if that will keep me from going blind, I'll do it.
Dr. Bello:	That's a good attitude, Mrs. Markus. Right now I need to go order you the correct eye drops. (*To the interpreter*): Interpreter, I need you to go over this fact sheet with the patient. I'll be back in a few minutes to finish up.	

Glaucoma Fact Sheet

About Glaucoma
1. Approximately three million people suffer from glaucoma.
2. Glaucoma is a leading cause of blindness for people over 60 years old.
3. Blindness from glaucoma can often be prevented with early treatment.

Early Stages
1. The early stages of the disease progress slowly with few or no symptoms.
2. Changes to your eyesight occur so gradually you might not notice them.
3. Early detection and treatment (with glaucoma eye drops, glaucoma surgery or both) can help preserve your vision.

Can glaucoma be cured?
- No. There is no cure for glaucoma. Vision lost from the disease cannot be restored.

Glaucoma Treatments Include:
1. Medicines, usually in the form of eye drops
2. Laser surgery
3. Conventional surgery

Medicines
1. Eye drops or pills are the most common early treatment for glaucoma.
2. Taken regularly, eye drops lower eye pressure.
3. Some medicines cause the eye to make less fluid.
4. Others lower pressure by helping fluid drain from the eye.
5. Before you begin glaucoma treatment, be sure to tell your eye care professional about other medicines and supplements that you are taking.
6. Glaucoma medicines need to be taken regularly as directed by your eye care professional.
7. Some medicines can cause side effects such as headaches and stinging, burning, or redness in the eyes.

Because glaucoma often has no symptoms, people may be tempted to stop taking, or may forget to take, their medicine. Regular use is very important.

SWITCH INTERPRETER

Dr. Bello:	Okay—all done with the fact sheet? Good. Mrs. Markus. Do you have any questions?	
Mrs. Markus:		No, I think I understand all that. But I'm sure I'll have more questions later on.
Dr. Bello:	Of course, and I'll be available to answer them any time. For now, let's get you started on these new eye drops. The nurse will be here in a minute to teach you how to apply them. And I would like you to come back next week so we can run a few more tests.	

Mrs. Markus:		Yes—I wanted to get started right away and make sure nothing happens to my eyesight. I'm very grateful, Dr. Bello. Thank you!
	[Nurse Hanson comes into the room. The person who was reading Dr. Bello's part will now be the nurse.]	
Nurse Hanson:	Hello there, Mrs. Markus. First I'm going to show you how to put in the drops and then I'll have the interpreter go over this instruction sheet with you, okay?	
Mrs. Markus:		Okay—but I'm a little nervous. Will it hurt?
Nurse Hanson:	The drops do sting just a little bit, but usually just for a few seconds, Most patients say they get used to them. Now, please tilt your head back and I'm going to put the drops in first.	
Mrs. Markus:		Ouch! That does sting! But I think I understand now how to put them in.
Nurse Hanson:	I'm glad to hear that. Now, the last thing before you go is to have the interpreter review these instruction with you. (to the interpreter) Interpreter, can you please read this information for Mrs. Markus?	

Administering Eye Drops for Eye Infections

Wash your hands and sit or stand in front of a mirror.

- Take off the top of the bottle.
- Bend your head backward and gently pull your lower eyelid down.
- Hold the dropper above one eye. Squeeze one drop into the pocket formed by gently pulling down the lower eyelid. Try not to touch your eye, eyelashes, or anything else with the dropper tip in order to keep it clean.
- Let go of the eyelid and keep the eye closed for as long as possible (2–3 minutes at least) after application of the eye drop, with your head tilted down toward the floor.
- Press gently on the tear duct (inner corner of the eye) with one finger for a minute.
- Wipe away any liquid that falls on to your cheek with a tissue.
- Repeat in the other eye if the drop is prescribed for both eyes.

When two different eye drop preparations are used at the same time of day, wait for at least five minutes before putting the second drop into an eye. This stops the first drop from being diluted or washed away.

MODE-SWITCHING ROLE PLAY B: The Diabetic Patient (English-Spanish)

Nurse practitioner:	Mrs. Covarrubias-Cruz, I am Asha Muppavarapu, a nurse practitioner. I want to talk to you about your diabetes a little bit.		
Patient:		Buenos días, doctora.	Good morning, doctor.
Nurse practitioner:	You look very nice today. I really like that color on you and your necklace is beautiful—is that from Santo Domingo?		
Patient:		No, doctora, es de Mérida, México. Tengo una prima que vive allí. Y gracias…al mal tiempo, buena cara.	No, doctor, it's from Merida, Mexico. I have a cousin who lives there. And, thank you; when things get rough, you have to keep your chin up.
Nurse practitioner:	Have you met with the diabetes educator and the nutritionist yet? Did they call you with those appointments?		
Patient:		No, no me llamaron. Paso casi todo el día en la casa, a menos que me vaya a la tienda de la esquina.	No, they didn't call me. I spend most of the day in the house, except when I go to the market on the corner.
Nurse practitioner:	It says here they tried to call you but they didn't reach you. Is this your number: 732-969-1276?		
Patient:		No, lo han apuntado mal. Es siete treinta y dos, tres nueve, doce, setenta y seis.	No, they wrote it down wrong. It is seven three two, three nine's, twelve, seventy-six
Nurse practitioner:	732, 39, 12, 76? It seems like you are missing a number.		

Patient:		No, doctora, discúlpeme. Tres nueve, o sea, nueve, nueve, nueve y el resto está bien.	No, doctor, I'm sorry. Three nines, meaning nine, nine, nine, and the rest is correct.
Nurse practitioner:	Oh, I see: 732-999-1276. I changed it and I'll ask them to call you to make an appointment. But we might also be able to set it up on your way out today.		
Patient:		Sí, eso sería mejor, de una vez, por favor, doctora.	Yes, please, that would be better, get it straight once and for all, doctor.
Nurse practitioner:	Well, as you remember when you came before, your sugar was very high and we gave you insulin and prescribed some pills to take.		
Patient:		Sí me acuerdo. Las tomé; las terminé como siempre me mandan a hacer con los antibióticos y ahora me siento mucho mejor. No sé si me dará otro ataque como el que me dio cuando me caí en el hospital.	Yes, I remember. I took them and I finished them, as I always do with the antibiotics. Now I feel much better. I don't know if I will have another attack, like the one that landed me in the hospital.
Nurse practitioner:	Are you still taking your medicines? You had three refills.		
Patient:		No, ya no. Yo no sabía de las repeticiones. Sí las terminé, seguro y me sentí mejor.	No, not anymore. I didn't know about the refills. I did take them and I felt better.
Nurse practitioner:	These pills are different, they are not like antibiotics for an infection. I know you were treated for latent TB too. But the pills I am giving you, you have to take them every day for life. You're diabetic now.		

Patient:		Bueno, yo no sabía. Sí me da la receta, las compro y las tomo.	Ok, I didn't know. If you give me another prescription, I'll buy them and take them.
Nurse practitioner:	All right. Your hemoglobin A1c today is very high. It's almost 13. Do you remember the finger stick that the nurse did when you came in? That was the A1c.		
Patient:		Sí, la muchacha me pinchó pero no sé para qué. Tampoco sé qué es la 'hemoglobina A-uno-ce.'	Yes, the young girl stuck me, but I don't know why. I don't know what the "hemoglobin A1c" is either.
Nurse practitioner:	Oh, I'm sorry. (looking in the computer system) I think we have a hand out that explains this, maybe I can print it. Fiddlesticks! Why won't this print? Oh well, maybe the interpreter could just translate what it says to you, ok? (to interpreter) Could you translate what it says to her?		
Patient:		Está bien, doctora, como quiera.	OK, doctor, whatever you like.

| Nurse practitioner: | (*Interpreter sight translates the following text on the screen*) "The Hemoglobin A1c is a common blood test that is done in either the lab or a doctor's office. It is used to measure the average level of blood sugar (glucose) over the past three months. There is no special preparation, like fasting, for example, that is required prior to this test. The purpose of this test is to determine if a patient's blood sugar is well controlled or not. If the results are less than 5.7% than the patient does not have diabetes; if the results are between 5.7% to 6.4%, the patient is consider pre-diabetic; and, if the results are higher than 6.5%, then the patient is considered diabetic. When the A1c result is higher than 7%, it means that your blood sugar is not well controlled and that you have the disease of diabetes. Your doctor will begin some type of treatment, which might only be a trial of diet and exercise but could also include taking medicine and even insulin. The higher the A1c is, the higher the risk of having heart problems, kidney problems, blindness and nerve damage." | | |

Patient:		(*patient interrupts, is upset and energetic at the same time*) ¡Espere! ¡O sea que cuando uno tiene diabetes, termina así, con esas enfermedades! Pensé que se me subía el azúcar por algo como una infección o algo así y que con unas pastillas se me iba a quitar. Creí que era algo pasajero, pero esto no lo puedo creer. No me dijeron nada de tener una enfermedad. ¡Dios mío! ¡No le explican nada aquí a uno, coño! Así murió mi padre, el pobrecito, que Dios lo bendiga, con sus riñones dañados y ciego, pero decían que era porque trabajaba en las minas de plata en Taxco, no por diabetes, no por lo que comía. ¡Por favor! Yo me voy a morir así también, ¿cierto? Yo sé que sí, aquí tan lejos de mi tierra, tan lejos de toda mi familia. Ya usé la insulina y ya tomé las pastillas, de hecho terminé el tratamiento. ¿Qué más me toca? ¿Qué más puedo hacer para evitar un fin tan maldito; tan infeliz? ¡¿Qué?!	(*patient interrupts, is upset and energetic at the same time*) Hold on! You mean that when you have diabetes, that is how you end up with those kinds of diseases! I thought my sugar was going up because of some infection, or something like that, and with taking some pills, it would go away, that it was temporary. But I can't believe this—I wasn't told anything about having a disease. Good God! Here they don't explain a damn thing to you! And that is just how my father died, poor soul, God bless him, blind and with bad kidneys but they always said that it was because he worked in the silver mines, not because of diabetes or what he ate. Please! I know that is how I am going to die—so far from my country, so far from my family. I already took insulin. I already took the pills; in fact, I finished the treatment. What else do I need to do? What else can I do to avoid such a damn miserable end? What?
Nurse practitioner:	Mrs. Covarrubias-Cruz, please calm down. I don't think you need to worry too much about the long-term effects right now. We can control them. Are you here with anyone?		
Patient:		¿Quién me va a esperar a mí? Yo vivo completamente sola	Who would be with me? I live totally alone.

Nurse practitioner:	I just thought it might help to include your husband or other family member.		
Patient:		Mi esposo, está muerto …	My husband's dead….
Nurse practitioner:	Ok, how about this? I think I can bring the diabetes educator in right now, and she speaks Spanish. I think she can go over this with you point by point. Would like that?		
Patient:		Bueno Doctora, como diga, ya que más me queda.	Yes, doctor, please.
Nurse practitioner:	I think the nurse is going to come in and give you some insulin as well, since your sugar right now is a little high. Will that be ok?		
Patient:		Sí claro, si la necesito, pues…	Yes, of course, if I need it.
Nurse practitioner:	I'll be right back, Mrs. Covarrubias-Cruz.		

Learning Activity 2.5(h): Practice in All Modes

Instructions

- Work in groups of three following the usual instructions for role plays.
- Your instructor will assign you any of the role plays in this chapter of the workbook that you have not yet had time to practice (or he or she can select role plays from any other chapter).
- Alternatively, your instructor may assign you role plays and practice activities from other sources.

Learning Objective 2.6

After completing this section and its corresponding exercises, the learner will be able to:
Objective 2.6(a)
- Understand the rationale, skills and requirements for consecutive note-taking.
Objective 2.6(b)
- Practice three effective techniques for note taking: apply a simplified Rozan technique; develop symbol and abbreviation systems and make skills automatic through repetitive practice materials.

 Learning Activity 2.6(a): Note-taking Practice: Taking a Baseline

Instructions

- The instructor will divide the group into pairs.
- The instructor will then read a patient story about diabetes.
- Close this workbook and do *not* read the story.
- When the instructor reads the story aloud, **both** members of the group will take notes.
- When so instructed, each member will then take turns interpreting the story back to his or her partner, reading from the interpreter's own notes.
- The instructor will then ask everyone to hold up their notes for the class to see. This is your baseline test. Keep your first notes to compare them with your last notes at the end of this lesson.

 Learning Activity 2.6(b): Note-taking Practice: Repetition

Instructions

- After the instructor gives a brief lecture on the Rozan's 7 principles of note-taking, the instructor will ask you to work in the same pairs as the previous exercise, Activity 2.6(a).
- The instructor will then read the same patient story you practiced to in Activity 2.6(a).
- Try to apply at least one of Rozan's principles as you take notes (taking notes vertically, using 1 or 2 symbols, drawing a line under each thought, etc).

- When so instructed, each member will then take turns interpreting the declaration back to his or her partner, reading off the interpreter's own notes.
- The instructor will conduct a brief group discussion to evaluate if participants were able to apply any of Rozan's principles.

 Learning Activity 2.6(c): Note-taking Practice: Basic symbols

Instructions

- Work in pairs.
- Using the diabetes stories from Learning Activity 2.6 (a), brainstorm symbols as directed below.
- When you have created several symbols, choose two or three and go to the flip chart or white board in the classroom and write them down to share with the class.

Symbols/abbreviation development:

Following the instructions and examples provided by working with your partner, create three to five symbols or abbreviations that will help you interpret diabetes stories in each of the following categories:

1. Symbols to indicate time and the passage of time
2. Symbols to indicate symptoms (fatigue, nausea, weight loss, thirst)
3. Symbols to indicate emotion (fear, anger, happiness, etc.)
4. Symbols to indicate emergency services (ER, EMTs, ambulance)
5. Symbols to indicate movement and travel
6. Symbols to create linkages between ideas (arrows, wavy lines, circles, etc.)

 Learning Activity 2.6(d): Note-taking Practice: Putting It All Together

Instructions

- The instructor will divide the group into pairs.
- The instructor will then read as many of the remaining patient stories as time permits.
- Close this workbook and do *not* read the statements below until instructed to do so.
- When the instructor reads a declaration out loud, **both** members of the group will take notes.
- Focus on practicing with one or two of Rozan's principles and one or two of the symbols you created. Repeat what worked in the first practices.
- When so instructed, each member will then take turns interpreting the declaration back to his or her partner, reading from the interpreter's own notes.
- At the end of this activity, the instructor will ask everyone to hold up their first and last notes to see the progress they made during the lesson.

For the instructor to read out loud[26]:

Patient Story #1: Our family will never forget the date of March 6, 2012. That was the day our 12-year-old son, Sam, was diagnosed with type 1 diabetes. For two weeks before that date, Sam complained of stomach aches and had vomited four times. We thought he had a stomach virus. But he got better and we thought everything was okay. Then one day Sam did not eat all day. He had a soccer game after school. He drank some punch and got sick right away. On the way home he fell asleep in the car. He kept sleeping all night until noon the next day. I got really scared and we took him to the doctor's. At the hospital we told the doctor about all of Sam's symptoms: having a fever, nausea, being thirsty a lot, being tired and sleeping for long periods. The doctor did several tests. He tested his urine and blood glucose. When the results came back he said he thought Sam had diabetes. It was terrible news. A huge shock. I cried a lot and was really scared. I didn't know much about diabetes. But now we know that people can live healthy lives with diabetes. Sam has learned how to give himself shots. He eats well and checks his blood sugar. He's still a normal kid.

Patient Story #2: When my daughter, Malina, was eight, I noticed she was eating more and was always thirsty. I got worried and I made an appointment with her doctor. He took some blood and ran tests. When we got the results he told us that Malina had type 1 diabetes. It was a horrible shock. But he taught us how to give her insulin shots and how to feed her a healthy diet. She had to take classes on nutrition too. At first I was really scared and angry. It was hard on all of us. But we learned how to plan Malina's diet. We all started eating better. The worst part was having to give her insulin shots three times a say. I hated having to poke my child with a needle, every day, day after day. When Malina saw how upset I was, she decided she wanted to learn how to give herself shots. Now she goes to school with her diabetes kit. She measures her blood glucose and gives herself shots.

Patient Story #3: The summer of 2008 is one our family will always remember. Our 16-year-old son, Han, started to change. He was tired. He would get agitated. He started to eat more and he was always thirsty. But he was losing weight. In July he went to football camp. He told us that he couldn't do it. The running and exercising were too much. We took a family trip to the Grand Canyon. Han couldn't hike back up the trail and when we went swimming, his heart beat really fast and he had a hard time breathing. He was always thirsty and had to go to the bathroom every half hour. On the way home he was so tired he couldn't get out of the car. We took him to the ER. The nurse asked us if we had considered diabetes as a way to explain his symptoms. After doing some blood and urine tests, the diagnosis was confirmed. His blood glucose level was 960. The first few months were hard. We had to learn how to count carbohydrates, give Han shots, monitor his blood sugars and change our diets. It took him a long time to gain back the weight he had lost. But after the first year, things got better. Han is playing sports again and he is no longer so upset.

Patient Story #4: Our daughter, Fatima, was diagnosed with diabetes when she was just four years old. She had the classic symptoms: fatigue, weight loss, extreme thirst, extreme hunger and she had to go to the bathroom all the time. We didn't know anything about diabetes. We thought she was growing a lot and was stressed because of starting a new school. One day I couldn't wake her up. I called 911 and Fatima was taken to the hospital in an ambulance. She spent three days in the intensive care unit. Then we all spent three days in the pediatric unit learning how to take care of her diabetes. Her daily routine has changed. She has to check her glucose when she wakes up, before breakfast, and at school before snack time, lunch and before activities. She has to poke her finger 10 times a day and give herself an injection four times a day. Fatima has two sisters. They help her with injections. Her oldest sister wants to be a doctor and find a cure for diabetes. I hope she does!

---

[26]Depending on the time available and other factors, the instructor may read only part of each story out loud.

LEARNING OBJECTIVES

After completing this chapter and its corresponding exercises, the learner will be able to:

OBJECTIVE 3.1

Unconscious Bias
Show awareness of bias while interpreting.

OBJECTIVE 3.2

Deciding When to Intervene
Apply four decision-making criteria to assess whether or not to mediate based on potential consequences for end users.

OBJECTIVE 3.3

Scripts for Mediation
Develop basic scripts for performing mediation in common situations in community interpreting.

OBJECTIVE 3.4

The Strategic Mediation Model
Practice five steps to perform strategic mediation.

OBJECTIVE 3.5

Cultural Competence and Strategic Mediation
Define cultural competence and demonstrate three strategies for performing strategic cultural mediation.

OBJECTIVE 3.6

Culturally Responsive Mediation
Develop techniques to perform effective, culturally responsive mediation.

Learning Objective 3.1

After completing this section and its corresponding exercises, the learner will be able to:

- Show awareness of bias while interpreting.

 Learning Activity 3.1(a): "The Interpreter's Dilemma" Role Plays

Instructions

- Work in groups of three following the usual instructions for role plays.
- Note that each script below includes a decision (or more than one decision) that the interpreter will have to make, including whether or not to intervene.
- Based on the response of the interpreter, when the script ends let the partners playing the provider and patient improvise by saying whatever feels natural.
- *Make sure the interpreter DOES NOT look at the script!*
- Let the first role play come to a natural conclusion.
- Write down what the interpreter chose to do at the end of the role play in the lines provided.
- Then, in your small group, answer the questions below the first role play.
- After that, go to the next role play and let someone else play the interpreter following the same instructions as above.

Role play #1: Mental health

Therapist:	Since this is our first visit, let me explain what I'd like to do today.	
Patient:		Thank you.
Therapist:	I'm hoping to hear what brought you here and what you may be experiencing.	
Patient:		All right
Therapist:	I'd like to hear how you're feeling physically and if you're sleeping well, how you're eating and so on. Can you tell me how you're feeling?	
Patient:		I'm having a hard time. I got here a year ago. My parents and my wife and my brother, they were all killed in the war.
Therapist:	Those are huge losses. I'm so sorry. A year doesn't seem like a long time. How are you feeling about it?	
Patient:		It's kind of hard to talk about. It's hurting a lot. I cry at night. I get a lot of nightmares about it.

112

Therapist:	You've obviously been through quite a lot. Is this sadness affecting you physically?	
Patient:		I get back pain a lot, in my lower back. I don't know if it's because of the sadness. (whispering) Interpreter, you come from my country, tell her about the spirits. I just <u>know</u> someone put a curse on me!

What did the interpreter in your role play group decide to do at the end of the script?

_____

_____

_____

Questions for this role play

7. How does the interpreter feel about his or her decision?
8. If the interpreter did *not* intervene, do you think s/he should have done so?
9. If the interpreter *did* intervene, did you agree with what he or she said?
10. What do you think is the most important thing an interpreter should try to do in a situation like this?

Role play #2: Insomnia

Nurse-practitioner:	So what brought you here today?	
Patient:		I—I don't know.
Nurse-practitioner:	I understand you're having some difficulty sleeping. Is that correct?	
Patient:		I—guess so.
Nurse-practitioner:	Can you tell me how long that's been going on?	
Patient:		I don't—I'm not—I don't really know.
Nurse-practitioner:	Can you describe to me how you're sleeping right now?	
Patient:		It's... hard to say.
Nurse-practitioner:	Uh—would you say you're sleeping seven to eight hours a night?	
Patient:		I'm not sure.
Nurse-practitioner:	(clearly getting frustrated) How many hours do you think you're sleeping?	

Patient:		It's... Well...
Nurse-practitioner:	Interpreter, I need to ask you something. I don't know what's going on here. Can you tell me if there's something cultural going on that I should know about? Or is this patient just mentally disturbed?	

What did the interpreter decide to do at the end of the script?

_____

_____

_____

Questions for this role play

- Did the interpreter interpret the nurse-practitioner's last statement? Why or why not?
- How does the interpreter feel about his or her decision?
- If the interpreter did *not* intervene, do you think s/he should have done so?
- If the interpreter *did* intervene, did you agree with what he or she said?
- What do you think is the most important thing an interpreter should try to do in a situation like this?

 Learning Activity 3.1(b): Implicit Bias

Instructions (Part A)

To explore your own bias, go to the world-famous website, Project Implicit, a project of Harvard University in the United States: https://implicit.harvard.edu/implicit/

Find the webpage with the implicit bias tests listed and choose a test: there are many different tests to explore one's bias regarding such issues as age, sexuality, gender, skin-tone, race, disability, and attitudes toward Asians, Arab-Muslims, among other topics. (It does not matter which test you choose.)

Take the test you selected following the online instructions. Each test should take you only a few minutes and you will get instant results.

Answer the questions below.

Questions

1. How did you feel about this test?

_____

_____

_____

2. What, if anything, surprised you about this test?

_____

_____

_____

3. What did you learn from taking the test?

_____

_____

_____

4. Would you recommend that others take one of the Project Implicit tests? Why or why not?

_____

_____

_____

Instructions (Part B)

- After taking at least one of the Project Implicit tests, if you are a practicing interpreter answer the following questions.
- It might also be helpful to take this list of questions and read them just before an interpreted session so you can monitor what you do in real life.
- Answer the questions as honestly as you can.
- Do not share your answers unless you wish to do so.

1. Do you introduce yourself to service providers in a different way than you do to service users? Why or why not? What, if anything, is different in your two introductions?

_____

_____

_____

2. Do you treat service providers with more respect than service users? Why or why not? What, if anything, is different about the way you treat service users and providers?

_____

_____

_____

3. Do you treat service users with higher levels of education with the same tone, posture, attitude and deference than you treat less-educated service users? Why or why not?

_____

_____

_____

4. Do you dress in a professional way that shows respect for all, even in settings like homeless shelters, nursing homes for elderly patients and domestic violence centers? Why or why not?

_____

_____

_____

5. Do you ever simplify a message for less-educated service users more often than you do with service users who have higher education levels? (Remember that you shouldn't simplify the message at all, for anyone—there are better ways to handle this type of situation.) Why or why not?

_____

_____

_____

6. Do you ever say one thing to a service provider when you intervene and something different to a service user? Why or why not?

_____

_____

_____

7. Have you ever softened rude, coarse or obscene language to avoid offending anyone? Why or why not?

_____

_____

_____

8. Let us say the following remark is made by a service provider speaking to an assistant about a patient or service user who is *present*.

Provider: *Her people are lazy, they never follow up. I wish they'd all go back to Africa.*

Would you interpret this remark?
   a.   Yes.
   b.   No.
   c.   Maybe.
   d.   I really don't know.

Justify your answer.

_____

_____

_____

After completing this section and its corresponding exercises, the learner will be able to:

- Apply four decision-making criteria to assess whether or not to mediate based on potential consequences for end users.

Criteria discussed in *The Community Interpreter®: An International Textbook* include:

1. Linguistic challenges
2. Role confusion
3. Cultural misunderstandings
4. Service system barriers

Examples

Although these areas of challenge can overlap, here is general guidance: a summary of pp. 215-222 of *The Community Interpreter®: An International Textbook*.

1. Linguistic challenges: Linguistic challenges come down to the interpreter's problems about the "linguistic envelope" (the words of the message), for example: you, the interpreter, do not understand something that was said or signed; you need to request a repetition; people speak over each other; someone does not understand an idiom or expression (though you interpreted it correctly); a baby is crying in the next room, making it difficult for you to hear, understand and analyze each message; you need a break for accuracy due to fatigue; you made a mistake and need to correct it.

2. Role confusion: Role confusion is a situation caused by someone not understanding your role, for example, someone asks you for an opinion or cultural guidance, wants you to fill out forms or translate documents you are not qualified to translate, requests your assistance (e.g., pushing a patient's wheelchair or helping someone reduce a major electric bill), asks you to sign as a witness or make a written report about the encounter (in a way that violates confidentiality), etc.

3. Cultural misunderstandings: Cultural misunderstandings are based on miscommunication across cultural differences between speakers with different worldviews. Common examples include:

- A cultural concept is unclear.
- The service user or patient's naming system is one the service provider doesn't know or understand (e.g., last name first, or including the maternal and paternal last names), but the provider is unaware of this difference.
- For cultural reasons, the service user doesn't ask questions, even when he or she doesn't understand the service provider.
- The service user does not understand how the service system works.
- The service user and provider are working with unidentified cultural assumptions, e.g., different understandings of what constitutes acceptable child discipline.
- A patient's lack of understanding about the culture of Western biomedicine, patient autonomy, preventive medicine or who should be informed about a fatal diagnosis (i.e., the patient or the patient's family).

- Providers' lack of understanding about what the patient believes has caused the illness.
  - Provider/service user expectations that the interpreter should act as a "cultural expert."
  - The desire to have the interpreter "explain" cultural issues.
  - Cultural concepts that have no equivalent in the target language.

4. Service system barriers: These are typically the challenges caused by the unfamiliarity of the service user with the service system and/or the provider's unfamiliarity with the equivalent service system in the service user's culture. There are many types of service system barriers. Here are just a few examples: providers who ask interpreters to take over a provider role (e.g., by explaining forms or procedures), treat minority service users in a discriminatory way. Also, service users may come to the interpreter privately to ask how the service system works or request help from the interpreter to surmount service system barriers.

Service system barriers can be logistic and also based on lack of understanding. For example, it is often assumed that service providers can write notes to the Deaf instead of bringing in a signed language interpreter, yet typically the official or national language is not the native language of the Deaf consumer.

 Learning Activity 3.2(a): "Should I Mediate?"

Instructions

- Work in small groups.
- Each group will read and discuss each scenario below.
- Circle the answer that reflects what you think you would *usually* do in the situation described (Parts 1 and 2).
- Decide which of the four criteria above (more than one criterion might apply) are relevant to each question: linguistic challenges; role confusion; cultural misunderstanding; or service system barriers.
- Not everyone in your group needs to have the same answers.

Part 1

If the patient or client doesn't seem to understand much, I would:
☐ Continue to interpret   ☐ Intervene   ☐ I'm not sure

If the provider or patient/client uses a term or phrase I don't understand, I would:
☐ Continue to interpret   ☐ Intervene   ☐ I'm not sure

If the provider is rude and abrupt, I would:
☐ Continue to interpret   ☐ Intervene   ☐ I'm not sure

If a doctor is prescribing medications to a patient who is fasting for religious reasons, and the doctor clearly does not know this, I would:

☐ Continue to interpret   ☐ Intervene   ☐ I'm not sure

If the patient/service user keeps speaking to me and not the service provider, I would:

☐ Continue to interpret   ☐ Intervene   ☐ I'm not sure

If the service provider does not clearly explain how the system works, and then leaves, and the patient/service user begs me to explain the issues myself, I would:

☐ Find someone to interpret for   ☐ Explain it myself   ☐ I'm not sure

If the provider is speaking in a very high register that seems impossible to interpret in a way that the patient or client will understand, and it is clear that the patient/service user will take the wrong follow-up action after the session (e.g., fail to fill out required paperwork or not prepare correctly for the surgery), I would:

☐ Continue to interpret   ☐ Intervene   ☐ I'm not sure

Learning Activity 3.2(b): Decision-making Criteria

Instructions

- Work in small groups.
- General community interpreters should select Scenarios: Section A of this activity.
- **Medical interpreters should select Scenarios: Section B.**
- Read each scenario together as a group.
- Decide whether or not to intervene and which criteria justify your group's decision.
- Answer the questions below each scenario.

Scenarios, Section A: General community interpreting

Note: As you answer the questions below, keep in mind that more than one of the four criteria could apply to any given scenario.

Education: A father is angry because the teacher is recommending that his child be tested to see if the child needs special services from a speech therapist for a speech delay. The father says he is convinced the child's problem is simply the language barrier. His child isn't "stupid" and doesn't need a "therapist." He gets so angry that he stands up and starts to shout.

Will you intervene? Why or why not? Which of the four criteria above might be relevant?

_____

_____

_____

Social services: At a homeless shelter, a family is leaving to live in a subsidized apartment. As a meeting with a shelter counselor ends, the mother turns to you and asks you for a loan of money to help the family. Clearly she's sure you won't interpret this message to the counselor (even though you made clear in your introduction that you would interpret everything—and you do interpret her message).

Will you intervene? Why or why not? Which of the four criteria above might be relevant?

_____

_____

_____

Education: The parents of a teenager have been called into the principal's office because their son damaged the locker of another boy and took some of that boy's possessions. The student apparently did so in anger, feeling that his girlfriend was "stolen" by the other boy. The principal explains to the parents that their son will be suspended and perhaps expelled. The parents are extremely angry. They insist this is all a cultural misunderstanding and that they are being discriminated against because they come from another country.

Will you intervene? Why or why not? Which of the four criteria above might be relevant?

_____

_____

_____

Social services: A domestic violence victim is staying at a shelter. When she meets a male paralegal who is trying to help her self-petition for legal residency independently of her abusive husband, she will not meet his eyes or answer his questions. You are aware that in her culture, many conservative women would not speak to a male person who they do not know well who is outside their family circles, and this woman is dressed in religiously conservative clothing.

Will you intervene? Why or why not? Which of the four criteria above might be relevant?

_____

_____

_____

Mental health: A torture treatment clinician (therapist) at a refugee resettlement center is meeting with a woman who was severely tortured. Now, for the first time, she shares her experience with the provider. She is so overwhelmed that she begins to cry, leans over and clutches your wrist, rocking back and forth as she weeps. She asks you if you have any tissues.

Will you intervene? Why or why not? Which of the four criteria above might be relevant?

_____

_____

_____

Scenarios, Section B: Medical interpreting

Health department: A patient is meeting with a nutritionist about changing her high-fat diet due to her gall bladder disease. The nutritionist gently scolds her for apparently not trying to follow the prescribed diet at all. The patient responds in monosyllables without explaining. You are aware that the recommended diet is completely different from the traditional foods eaten by most people in the patient's country of origin. You suspect that it might be difficult for the patient, who did not graduate from elementary school and is not literate, to understand and follow a restrictive diet plan, far less adopt one filled with very unfamiliar and perhaps unappetizing foods.

Will you intervene? Why or why not? Which of the four criteria above might be relevant?

_____

_____

_____

Hospital, preparation for anesthesia: During the appointment, the nurse practitioner indicates that she will leave the room, meaning that you will be alone with the patient. You know this is unwise because the patient is likely to draw you into a conversation which, in addition to eroding professional boundaries, could involve sharing medical information with you that she has not shared with the nurse practitioner.

Will you intervene? Why or why not? Which of the four criteria above might be relevant?

_____

_____

_____

Pediatric urology: A urologist is trying to explain to parents from a country with traditional gender-assigned roles that their baby was born with an undetermined gender. The urologist speaks in technical language about chromosomes and the medical condition, and it seems clear to you, the interpreter, that the parents have no idea what the doctor is saying. The doctor clearly is not aware that the parents are confused. You might be wrong, but you are fairly convinced that the parents are lost.

Will you intervene? Why or why not? Which of the four criteria above might be relevant?

_____

_____

_____

Instructions

- Read the dialogues below.
- Answer the questions that follow each dialogue.

Dialogue A

School psychologist: Mrs. Levian, I'm happy you could come and talk to me about Abi today. But you look like you've had an accident. Are you all right?

Mother: Oh, fine, yes.

School psychologist: You're sure?

Mother: Yes, yes. I'm sure. Please continue.

Circle the answer you find best.

You, the interpreter, just interpreted yesterday for this same woman at a domestic violence shelter. You know that her husband beat her up so severely she was in the hospital. Will you:

    Simply interpret?   Intervene?   Speak to the provider outside the session?

Explain your answer:

_____

_____

_____

Dialogue B

Nurse: We'd like to offer you an epidural.

Patient giving birth: (*panting*) No, no, I don't want it.

Nurse: But you seem to be in serious pain. Are you sure you don't want the epidural?

Patient: Yes. I don't want problems later.

Nurse: Well, it's your decision.

Circle the answer you find best.

You, the interpreter, know that the patient is confusing epidurals with something often used in rural hospitals in the country where the patient comes from: a spinal block. Many patients from this country believe an epidural is a spinal block and will bring on serious complications, including long-term back problems or even paralysis, which is not accurate. Will you:

      Simply interpret?   Intervene?   Speak to the provider outside the session?

Explain your answer:

_____

_____

_____

Dialogue C

Sexual assault counselor: I'm glad you were able to come in today.

Client: Thank you.

Sexual assault counselor: Have you ever been to a sexual assault center before?

Client: No.

Sexual assault counselor: Then let me explain how all this works. This first meeting with me today is what we call an intake, and now that you've already filled out the form you and I will talk for about an hour. And then based on how you're feeling and what you need, we'll talk about what you'd like to do next, what we recommend, what openings we have and the financial resources that might be available. For example, we never turn away anyone based on ability to pay and we have a sliding scale, but we do have limited resources, so depending whether you see a therapist or join a group session or whatever you decide, there might be a waiting list for that service. Is that clear so far?

Circle the answer you find best.

You, the interpreter, are aware that what the sexual assault counselor is explaining simply does not exist in the patient's culture. The idea of "sliding scale" (different charges based on one's income), therapy or counseling, what a therapist is, what groups sessions are, the idea of a waiting list—all these are culturally unfamiliar concepts that the patient, you suspect, doesn't understand. Will you:

      Simply interpret?   Intervene?   Speak to the provider outside the session?

Explain your answer:

_____

_____

_____

Instructions

- Choose one or both of the longer dialogue or the real-life scenario below.
- Answer the questions that follow the dialogue and/or the scenario.

Ophthalmologist:	Any particular problems you're coming to see me about or will this be pretty routine?	
Patient:		No, nothing special. I have to get my eyes checked for my job.
Ophthalmologist:	What do you do?	
Patient:		I'm a truck driver.
Ophthalmologist:	Okay. I was just going over your insurance information. Can you tell me the last time you had an eye exam?	
Patient:		About five years ago I think.
Ophthalmologist:	You don't wear glasses or contact lenses?	
Patient:		Nope. My daughter has contacts.
Ophthalmologist:	Do you have any special eye problems you think I should know about?	
Patient:		Just the usual. I'm getting older. It's getting harder to see.
Ophthalmologist:	Okay, well, I'll need to take a bit of history. Just a few questions and please just let me know if you don't understand anything.	
Patient:		OK.
Ophthalmologist:	First, do you have any history of diabetes or high blood pressure?	
Patient:		No.
Ophthalmologist:	Any history of a serious eye infection or eye injury?	
Patient:		Not that I can remember.

Ophthalmologist:	What about any times you might have had eye pain, or red eyes, or eye discharge?	
Patient:		Sometimes I get red eyes when I'm short of sleep. That's all.
Ophthalmologist:	Any family history of eye problems with your mom or dad or your grandparents?	
Patient:		I don't really know… I think my mother had something on her eyes before she died.
Ophthalmologist:	I don't mean cataracts. Did any of your older relatives have glaucoma or macular degeneration?	
Patient:		My mother… I just can't remember. Not cataracts. Something bad.
Ophthalmologist:	Anything like neovascular macular degeneration? Or choiroidal neovascularization— CNV?	
Patient:		I don't know.
Ophthalmologist:	What about you? Reading, for example. Do you have trouble reading fine print?	
Patient:		Uh—
Ophthalmologist:	Or do your eyes get tired when you read?	
Patient:		Um…
Ophthalmologist:	Tell me how your eyes feel when you read for a long time.	
Patient:		I—I don't know…
Ophthalmologist:	Okay. Now what I'd like is to have you look at that chart over there. Do you see it? I'm going to put this shield over one eye and cover it up. So using your other eye, just read the letters for me.	

Note: You, the interpreter, know this patient from other appointments. You know that the patient is not literate and is very embarrassed about this. Will you intervene? Why or why not? What will you say?

_____

_____

_____

How would you apply the CHIA[27] Ethical Decision-making Process (CHIA, 2002, pp. 55-61) to the interpreter's dilemma in the glaucoma dialogue? (Note that these CHIA guidelines are discussed in *The Community Interpreter®: An International Textbook* in both Chapter 1 and Chapter 3. In Chapter 3 they are discussed on pp. 223-224.) To review, the steps in the CHIA process are as follows:

- *Ask questions to determine whether there is a problem.* [We strongly recommend that you ask these questions silently, in the privacy of your own mind.]
- Identify and clearly state the problem, considering the ethical principles that may apply and ranking them in applicability.
- Clarify personal values as they relate to the problem.
- Consider alternative actions, including benefits and risks.
- Decide to carry out the action chosen.
- Evaluate the outcome and consider what might be done differently next time.

School health aide scenario

Now let's look at a real-life situation and apply the CHIA ethical decision-making guidelines. Consider this scenario.
- A child at school is feeling unwell.
- He goes to the sick room.
- A school health aide notices the child has strange red marks on his chest.
- When the child's mother arrives, an interpreter comes in to interpret.
- The interpreter has often seen these exact types of marks; she knows that they are the result of a healing technique called coining, which involves rubbing hot coins over a sick person's body.
- The interpreter sees that the school health aide and mother are confused; she fears that the school health aide is going to call a local government agency responsible for child protective services.
- She fears that the telephone call may trigger a legal investigation and even an arrest (many arrests in the United States, for example, are caused by coining of children).

Note: This example reflects a situation where *any* interpreter for that language would recognize this cultural practice. (That is certainly not the case for all cultural practices; see Section 3.6 on Culturally Responsive Mediation for examples of more complex cases.) If the interpreter is 100 percent certain that these marks show evidence of a healing practice and not child abuse, should

---

[27]CHIA is the California Healthcare Interpreting Association. To download a copy of the document that contains the ethical decision-making guidelines, California Standards for Healthcare Interpreters, go to www.chiaonline.org or http://www.chiaonline.org/?page=CHIAStandards

the interpreter interrupt the session to say anything about coining to the school health aide? If so, what would be appropriate to say? Are there any legal considerations here?

To answer these questions, look at the six CHIA ethical decision-making steps, trying to adapt them to the cultural context you are working in. (If you have not yet interpreted in real-life settings, do your best to imagine how you would—or should—respond.)

CHIA Step 1. Ask questions to determine whether there is a problem.

Focus on the consequences if you do not intervene. Here are examples of the questions you could ask yourself: *What will happen if I just interpret and do not speak up? Does the school health aide look suspicious of child abuse? If I don't say anything, will she call the government child protection services agency?* (**Note:** In the United States, in most states a health aide who even suspects child abuse will be legally required to report the parent to Child Protective Services, a practice that has led to many arrests and other serious consequences for immigrant parents who practice coining with their children.)

Now imagine you are the interpreter. Write down the questions you might ask yourself in real life here:

_____

_____

_____

_____

_____

_____

CHIA Step 2. Identify and clearly state the problem, considering the ethical principles that may apply and ranking them in applicability.

Here are some examples of ethical principles involved in this situation (referring to the document about community interpreter ethics and standards at the beginning of the textbook (pp. 3-30) and also the NCIHC *National Code of Ethics for Interpreters in Health Care*):

- *Intercultural communication/cultural awareness.* Is it part of your responsibility as an interpreter to speak up about cultural differences that you may observe? Do you have a responsibility to speak out to protect an individual from serious harm due to a cultural misunderstanding?
- *Impartiality.* If you intervene to address this issue, are you acting impartially? Why or why not? Would you be seen as taking sides if you address the problem?
- *Professional boundaries.* If you intervene to address the communication problem, are you overstepping your role boundaries? Would your answer change if this was an interview for legal interpreting (e.g., a legal investigation of suspected child abuse by an investigator with the local government)?

- *Transparency.* If you do intervene, will you be able to do so in a way that is completely transparent? Is what you plan to tell one party (the nurse) exactly what you will report to the other party (the parent)?
- *Professional conduct/professionalism.* Should a professional interpreter get involved in a situation that might become a legal situation? Is the general understanding of professional interpreters in your country or region that community interpreters *should* address this type of misunderstanding?

These are just some of the ethical issues that might face you in a situation like this one. Now find the code of ethics for your own country or region and select those ethical principles that you think could apply here, using your own justification. (**Note:** U.S. and medical interpreters will ideally select the NCIHC *A National Code of Ethics for Interpreters in Health Care* discussed in Chapter 1 of *The Community Interpreter®: An International Textbook* and this workbook and available at www.ncihc.org.)

_____
_____
_____
_____
_____
_____

CHIA Step 3. Clarify personal values as they relate to the problem.

In this type of situation you may feel strong pressure from others and yourself to do "the right thing." You might feel that people of the parent's culture are often discriminated against and misunderstood. Perhaps you do not want to contribute to such problems by failing to take action. Perhaps your spiritual beliefs suggest that you should try to prevent harm. Each interpreter's values are different and personal.

Write down your own personal values as they relate to the problem under discussion.

_____
_____
_____
_____

CHIA Step 4. Consider alternative actions, including benefits and risks.

If you remain silent, *what may happen*? Is there really a risk of arrest for the parents? What *are* the risks that you see for the parent? The child? The school? If you intervene and try to explain or address the cultural issue, what happens if it turns out that the parent *is* abusive?

Write down the benefits and risks that seem most likely to you in the context of your own country or region if (a) the interpreter does not speak up about coining practices in this situation; or (b) intervenes to perform a cultural mediation about coining.

_____

_____

_____

_____

CHIA Step 5. Decide to carry out the action chosen.

You make a decision. For the sake of argument, let's say that you are a Vietnamese or Hmong interpreter who is extremely familiar with this type of practice and you feel 100 percent sure that the marks on the child correspond to the cultural practice of coining. You decide to intervene. You say to the health aide, "Excuse me, as the interpreter, I wondered if you are familiar with coining." Then you tell the parent, "As the interpreter, I just asked the nurse if she was familiar with coining." The health aide says, "No, I'm not. What is coining?" and you *do not answer her*. Instead, you interpret her question, and let the *mother* explain what coining is.

Do you agree with this way of approaching the cultural issue? Why or why not?

_____

_____

_____

_____

CHIA Step 6. Evaluate the outcome and consider what might be done differently next time.

Now let us say that the health aide, after the interpreter intervenes, asks the mother more questions to determine what really happened. The health aide learns what coining is. The health aide does *not* report the mother to Child Protective Services. Instead she reports this information to a nurse who conducts a physical examination of the child and refers the child to a doctor who diagnoses bronchitis, a condition unrelated to the marks.

What do you think of this outcome? If you were the interpreter, after hearing this outcome, would you take the same action described above in a similar situation? Why? If not, what would you do differently and why?

_____

_____

_____

_____

Learning Objective 3.3

After completing this section and its corresponding exercises, the learner will be able to:

- Develop basic scripts for performing mediation in common situations in community interpreting.

 Learning Activity 3.3(a): Record a Sample Mediation Script

Instructions

- Take out a recording device, such as a mobile telephone, recorder or MP3 player.
- Test it.
- Select at least two of the four situations below.
- **Medical interpreter should select scripts #1 and #4.**
- Read out loud *and record* the first script that you chose, speaking it in *both your working languages.*
- Listen to your recording.
- Fill out the form below the script.
- Then do the same for one more script.

Situation and script #1

Situation: The doctor explained prescription instructions in complicated language. You are very afraid the patient did not understand the instructions and may take the wrong dosage.

Script #1

Speaking to the doctor:
Excuse me, as the interpreter I'm worried that what I'm interpreting about the medication isn't clear.

Speaking to the patient:
Excuse me, as the interpreter I told the doctor I'm worried that what I'm interpreting about the medication isn't clear.

Situation and script #2

Situation: A municipal sanitation employee is explaining recycling requirements to a restaurant owner. He uses the word "commingled," which you think means that the restaurant owner has to recycle metal, paper and certain kinds of plastic together in one container (but even you are slightly confused).

Script #2

Speaking to the restaurant owner:
Excuse me, as the interpreter I'm not sure the meaning of "commingled" is very clear. Maybe if you explain, I can interpret it more clearly.

Speaking to the sanitation employee:
Excuse me, as the interpreter I just told the sanitation representative that I'm not sure the meaning of "commingled" is very clear. I told him that maybe if he explains, I can interpret it more clearly.

Self-evaluation form for mediation practice: Script #2

Circle the best answer that describes your opinion of your performance.

Was my delivery:
    a.   Fast or slow?
    b.   Smooth or stumbling?
    c.   Convincing or awkward?
    d.   Weaker in one language than the other?

Did my tone sound:
    a.   Respectful or harsh?
    b.   Kind or abrupt?
    c.   Different in any way when speaking to the doctor vs. the patient? If so, describe the differences:

_____

_____

What would *I* say that would sound more natural for this mediation, in both languages? (Use the kind of wording that you think you might really say in a similar real-life situation.)

_____

_____

_____

Situation and script #3

Situation: A school principal has called in a mother because police are investigating a report of vandalism and asking questions of the parent's child. Although the principal says the child is *not* implicated in the crime, you get the strong sense that the parent thinks the child may be arrested (and deported) because she doesn't understand "implicated" in her own language. The mother isn't saying so: you see the terror in her eyes and you know her cultural community very well.

Script #3

Speaking to the police officer:
Excuse me, the interpreter suggests there may be a break in communication about what "implicated in a crime" means.

Speaking to the parent:
Excuse me, the interpreter suggested there may be a break in communication about what "implicated in a crime" means.

Self-evaluation form for mediation practice: Script #3

Circle the best answer that describes your opinion of your performance.

Was my delivery:
- a. Fast or slow?
- b. Smooth or stumbling?
- c. Convincing or awkward?
- d. Weaker in one language than the other?

Did my tone sound:
- a. Respectful or harsh?
- b. Kind or abrupt?
- c. Different in any way when speaking to the doctor vs. the patient? If so, describe the differences:

_____

_____

What would *I* say that would sound more natural for this mediation, in both languages? (Use the kind of wording that you think you might really say in a similar real-life situation.)

_____

_____

_____

Situation and script #4

Situation: The patient referred to a kind of tea she has been taking (calling it green tea) when you feel sure she means a traditiona herbal tea that might contain substances potentially contraindicated or capable of interacting with a prescription. The doctor hasn't noticed and clearly thinks the patient is referring to regular green tea.

Script #4

Speaking to the doctor:
Excuse me, the interpreter recommends asking the patient about this kind of tea.

Speaking to the patient:
Excuse me, the interpreter recommended that the doctor ask you about this kind of tea.

Self-evaluation form for mediation practice: Script #4

Circle the best answer that describes your opinion of your performance.

Was my delivery:
   a.   Fast or slow?
   b.   Smooth or stumbling?
   c.   Convincing or awkward?
   d.   Weaker in one language than the other?

Did my tone sound:
   a.   Respectful or harsh?
   b.   Kind or abrupt?
   c.   Different in any way when speaking to the doctor vs. the patient? If so, describe the differences:

_____

_____

What would *I* say that would sound more natural for this mediation, in both languages? (Use the kind of wording that you think you might really say in a similar real-life situation.)

_____

_____

_____

 Learning Activity 3.3(b): Write Basic Mediation Scripts

So far, you have seen some examples of basic mediation scripts. But they are not written in *your* language: in other words, they are not the mediation scripts *you* would probably use in real life.

When you perform strategic mediation as an interpreter, you will need to plan scripts that feel natural for you and that fit your social, cultural and professional context. This exercise will help you to develop your own mediation scripts.

Instructions

- Working with the situations below, write your own mediation scripts in the blank lines *in at least two working languages* (one for when you address the service provider and a different language for when you address the patient).
- **DO NOT LOOK AT PART 2 below!!**
- Working in pairs who share the same working languages (if possible), read your scripts out loud to your partner.
- Then read Part 2 below.
- Make changes to your scripts as you see fit by writing new scripts in the lines provided.

- Read the new scripts out loud.
- Flag the scripts that you like the best.
- **Medical interpreters:** Skip question 4 below.

Note: Mediation scripts below follow the order *provider* and then *patient/client*. However, in real life there is no prescribed order. You may intervene with the patient first or the client, as you choose (Legal interpreters, however, should address the legal service provider first when intervening. Interpreters in mental health should speak to the therapist or clinician first.)

Part 1: Write scripts

1. The client uses a phrase or expression that you do not understand.

When you mediate, what will you say to the provider?

_____

_____

_____

What will you say to the client?

_____

_____

_____

2. The client appears confused, probably because the provider is speaking in very formal language (high register), but you are not allowed to simplify the provider's message. Assume, in this case, that you decide you should mediate.

When you mediate, what will you say to the provider?

_____

_____

_____

What will you say to the client?

_____

_____

_____

3. While you are interpreting, the provider uses a term like "speech sound disorder" (in education), "financial qualification form" (in human services) or "advance directive" (in healthcare). You could interpret the term literally but it would have no meaning for the client and you are not aware of an equivalent term in the client's language. **Note:** Do **not** explain the term to the client yourself.

When you mediate, what will you say to the provider?

_____

_____

_____

What will you say to the client?

_____

_____

_____

4. You are interpreting in a school for a parent-teacher conference when it becomes clear to you that the parent has no concept of what a progress report is because in the parent's village the school didn't have this type of report. You feel that this is a cultural barrier and decide to mediate.

When you mediate, what will you say to the teacher?

_____

_____

_____

What will you say to the parent?

_____

_____

_____

5. At a health department, the nurse is asking many personal questions. As the interpreter, you can tell the patient is getting shocked and offended, especially the questions about how many sexual partners the patient had. The patient keeps asking you why the nurse is asking a respectable married woman all these questions. You interpret her questions, but after the third time she speaks to you as the interpreter, you realize that you need to clarify your role to her so that she directs questions only to the nurse.

When you mediate, what will you say to the nurse?

_____

_____

_____

What will you say to the patient?

_____

_____

_____

6. The patient or client makes reference to a belief known as the "hot and cold foods." You are aware that the expression can mean many things and that the provider is probably not familiar with the concept. The cultural belief is relevant to the service.

When you mediate, what will you say to the provider?

_____

_____

_____

What will you say to the patient?

_____

_____

_____

Part 2: Evaluate your scripts

As you look at the possible answers below, keep in mind that there is no single correct way of writing mediation scripts for any given scenario. Each interpreter in real life will say something different. Therefore the suggestions in the answer sheet below are just that: suggestions.

When you compare your answers to the answers below see if you want to make any changes to your answers above. In other words, revise your script to help it reflect whatever you like best about your own script and what you like best about any of the scripts below. But try to make what you write sound like something you would say in real life.

Answer sheet

The following answers are examples only. The answers that you wrote yourself may be excellent. When you compare your answers to these answers, try to keep your own, natural language but borrow any content or elements of the answers below that you find helpful or important.

1. The patient/client uses a phrase or expression you do not understand.
To the provider: <u>Excuse me, the interpreter needs to ask the patient to clarify the meaning of [the expression, in its original language].</u>
To the patient/client: <u>Excuse me, the interpreter needs to ask you what [the expression] means?</u>

2. The patient/client appears confused, probably because the provider is speaking in very formal language (high register), but you are not allowed to simplify the provider's message.
To the provider: <u>Excuse me, as the interpreter, I'm concerned that what I'm interpreting isn't clear.</u>
To the client: <u>Excuse me, the interpreter just told the provider that I'm concerned that what I'm interpreting isn't clear.</u>

3. While you are interpreting, the provider uses a term like "speech sound disorder" (in education), "financial qualification form" (in human services) or "advance directive" (in healthcare). You could interpret literally but it would have no meaning for the client and you are not aware of an equivalent term in the client's language.

To the provider: <u>Excuse me, the interpreter is unaware of an equivalent in language [X] for [the term].</u>
To the patient/client: <u>Excuse me, as the interpreter I just told the provider I'm concerned there may be no equivalent in your language for [the term in English].</u>

4. You are interpreting in a school for a parent-teacher conference when it becomes clear to you that the parent has no cultural concept of what a progress report is because in the parent's village the school didn't have this type of report.
To the teacher: <u>Excuse me, the interpreter suggests the meaning of *progress reports* may not be clear.</u>
To the parent: <u>Excuse me, the interpreter suggested the meaning of *progress reports* may not be clear.</u>

5. At a health department, the nurse is asking many personal questions. As the interpreter, you can tell the patient is getting shocked and offended, especially the questions about how many sexual partners the patient had. The patient keeps asking you why the nurse is asking a respectable married woman all these questions. You interpret her questions, but after the third time she speaks to you as the interpreter, you realize you need to clarify your role to her.
<u>To the nurse: Excuse me, as the interpreter I need to clarify my role with the patient and ask her to direct her questions to you.</u>
To the patient: <u>Excuse me, as the interpreter I can't answer questions. May I ask you to direct your questions to the provider, not to me.</u>

138

6. The patient or client makes reference to a belief known as the "hot and cold foods." You are aware that the expression can mean many things and that the provider is probably not familiar with the concept. This belief is relevant to the service being provided.

To the provider: <u>Excuse me, the interpreter recommends you ask the patient what "hot and cold foods" mean to her.</u>

To the patient/client: <u>Excuse me, as the interpreter I recommended that the provider ask what "hot and cold foods" mean to you.</u>

 Learning Activity 3.3(c): Mediation Script Role Play

Instructions

- In groups of three, assign roles for the role play below.
- Act out the role play.
- Make sure the interpreter does not see the script!
- Someone who is *not* playing the interpreter should write down what the interpreter actually says during the mediation section in the middle. For purposes of this role play, *assume that the interpreter SHOULD intervene.*
- After finishing the role play, discuss what you think the interpreter *should* say and write a script in both languages.
- Now act out the role play again with a different person playing the interpreter.
- After finishing the role play this second time, assess: did the interpreter use the script you discussed together? Why or why not?

Mediation role play script: Herpes (English-Spanish)

GYN Resident	Ok, Ms. Ramirez, tell me, why did you come in today?		
Patient		Vine porque tengo herpes y estoy muy alterada. Tengo unos granitos muy feos y me duelen. No tiene idea de la vergüenza que tengo.	I'm here today because I have herpes and I'm real upset. I have some nasty blisters and they hurt. You have no idea how embarrassed I am.
GYN Resident	Who told you that you have herpes?		
Patient		Así me dijeron en la otra clínica antes de que cerraran. Me dijeron que viniera aquí.	That's what I was told at the other clinic before it closed. They told me to come here.
GYN Resident	You said you had a rash. Where do you have it?		
Patient		En toda la espalda…	All over my back…
GYN Resident	(looks at patient's back) Yes, Ms. Ramirez, you have herpes zoster. They were right. That's definitely what it is…I have your chart from there.		
Patient		¡Ay, Dios Miomío! Tenían razón… ¿Qué voy a hacer ahora? Doctor, Dígame, ¿hay cura?	Oh, my God! They were right…Now what am I going to do? Doctor, tell me, is there a cure?
GYN Resident	You'll have to go see the internal medicine doctor here, and he can treat you.		
Patient		¿Por qué al médico general si lo que tengo es herpes? ¡No puedo creer esto! Necesito un tratamiento ahorita. Ya hasta dejé a mi novio porque quiero salir de todo esto.	Why an internal medicine doctor, if it's herpes? I can't believe this! I need treatment right now. I even left my boyfriend so that I could get past this.
GYN Resident	Well you can make an appointment today, and they'll probably see you next week. Herpes zoster can be treated with medicine, but there is no cure.		

Patient		¡Dios mío! No diga eso. Rento un cuarto en una casa con una familia que tiene niños y compartimos el baño— ¿esto les puede seguir? Era por mi novio, el me contagió de herpes y por eso lo dejé.	Good God! Don't say that! I rent a room from a family that has children and we share the bathroom—can the kids get this from me? This was because of my boyfriend, he is the one who gave me herpes and that is why I left him.
GYN Resident	Hold on—you don't have herpes, the STI, but herpes zoster, also known as shingles.		
Patient		Entonces, ¿no tengo esa enfermedad? ¡Gracias a Dios! Y ahora, ¿qué le digo a mi novio?	So I don't have it? Thank God! Now, what should I tell my boyfriend?
GYN Resident	Well, that I don't know. I'm sorry. Please wait here for the nurse to discharge you and don't forget the appointment with the internal medicine doctor.		

Learning Objective 3.4

After completing this section and its corresponding exercises, the learner will be able to:
- Practice five steps to perform strategic mediation.

 Learning Activity 3.4(a): Unscramble the Steps for Strategic Mediation

Instructions

- Below you will find the five steps of the Strategic Mediation Model in the *incorrect* order.
- In the blank lines provided, *without* consulting your textbook, write them in the correct order.
- Consult p. 238 of ***The Community Interpreter®: An International Textbook*** to see if your answers are correct.

"Scrambled" steps

- Mediate briefly.
- Resume interpreting.
- Report your mediation to the other party.
- Interpret what was just said or signed.
- Identify yourself as the interpreter.

Steps in the correct order:

1. _____

2. _____

3. _____

4. _____

5. _____

 Learning Activity 3.4(b): Practice the Steps for Strategic Mediation

Instructions

- Below you will find the five steps of the Strategic Mediation Model as they are applied to basic requests for clarification.
- Clarification is one of the easiest and simplest forms of mediation: use these examples to practice the five steps for the Strategic Mediation Model.
- Select Section A or B below; medical interpreters should select Section B.
- If possible, practice in groups of three so that you are pretending to be in the middle of a session.
- Use the example provided and apply that model to the other scenarios listed below it.

Note: In some cases you would request clarification because you do not understand a term or phrase being used. In other cases, you might request clarification because you are concerned that the service user or patient doesn't understand and that the consequences could be serious. Either way, you can follow the same steps. Also, be aware that for convenience, the examples below are about service providers, but often service users use terms that are unfamiliar to you; so of course you can request clarification from service users or patients too.

Example

Use this example to guide your practice of the five steps for strategic mediation:

Doctor: I think we'll need to do a fine-needle biopsy.

Interpreter
Step 1: [raise your hand and interpret the doctor's statement into the patient's language *but*

keep "fine-needle biopsy" in English or the source language] I think we'll need to do a fine-needle biopsy.
Steps 2 and 3: [*say this to the doctor*]: Excuse me, doctor, as the interpreter, may I ask you to clarify what "fine-needle biopsy" means?
Step 4: [*say this to the patient*] Excuse me, as the interpreter, I just asked the doctor to clarify what "fine-needle biopsy" means.

Doctor: Sure, I'd be happy to explain. It's a medical test where a thin, hollow needle is inserted into a lump or mass to take a sampling of cells there, typically to check for cancer.

Interpreter (*interprets into the patient's language*)
[Step 5] Sure, I'd be happy to explain. It's a medical test where a thin, hollow needle is inserted into a lump or mass to take a sampling of cells there, typically to check for cancer.

Section A: General clarification practice

- Social worker: We need you to fill out this *financial qualification form* and the *waiver*.
- Healthcare: Hmm, this looks like a *hematoma*.
- Domestic violence: You need a *protection order*, not a *restraining order*.
- Therapy: It sounds like you're having *flashbacks*.
- Education: You'll need to attend a *school board hearing* about your child's *possible expulsion*.

Section B: Healthcare clarification practice

School nurse: Hmm. This looks like a *hematoma*.
Gastroenterologist: So I'm going to refer you for a *double-contrast barium enema*.
OB-GYN: We also need the blood draw to rule out *toxiplasmosis*.
Nurse: Take this cup for the urine sample. We need a *mid-stream specimen*.
Chiropractor: Your *X-ray* showed some *bone spurs* that seem to indicate *cervical spondylosis*.

Learning Activity 3.4(c): Body Language and Mediation: Video Recording

Instructions

- Select one of the two role plays below.
- **Medical interpreters will select Role Play B.**
- Set up video recording using a smartphone, a camera or another device.
- In groups of four, act out the role play following the usual instructions but have the fourth person record the role play.
- The interpreter *must not see the script.*
- The interpreter should perform at least one mediation: a request for clarification of *collection agency* (in Role Play A) and *DUI* (in Role Play B).
- After completing the role play, let everyone in your group watch the video.
- At the end of the each role play there are questions for your group to answer. *Do not read the questions before you view the video.*
- If time permits, do the same role play or another role play following the same instructions with a different person playing the interpreter.

Role play A: The angry library patron

Note: Before this role play begins, make sure you tell the interpreter this information:

You, the interpreter, have interpreted for this patron before. You know that the family gets food from a food bank because they have no money. They are living day to day. Both parents are unemployed. Things are desperate. The library fine mentioned in this role play will be impossible for them to pay.

Staff member:	How can I help you?	
Patron:		I'm very upset. Look, I just got a threatening letter about a library fine! And the fine is for $150!
Staff member:	(glances at letter, rustling of paper) Hmm, yes, I see what's going on. This letter is from a collection agency[28] that we use, Exclusive Management System.	
	INTERPRETER SHOULD REQUEST CLARIFICATION OF "COLLECTION AGENCY"—remind the interpreter, if necessary.	

---

[28]A collection agency, or debt collector, is a type business that collects payments of debts. Most of these agencies get a fee (such as a percentage of the total amount) from the creditors who want their money from the individual or business that owes the debt.

Patron:		Collection agency? For a library?
Staff member:	Yes, it's a company that we give the bill to when you don't pay. That's what it does. It collects payments from people who don't pay. Unfortunately, the fact that you didn't pay the library and this bill went to a collection agency does go on your credit report.	
Patron:		My credit report? You mean, I get a black mark on my credit? So if we want to get a new apartment, the leasing company will see the black mark and maybe we don't get the apartment?
Staff member:	Uh…I mean…I guess you'd have to call the credit report bureau to find that out.	
Patron:		That means yes! We get a poor credit rating. This is crazy! For a few kid videos!
Staff member:	I can see you ran up quite a fine there. But did you know you can renew in person, by telephone or online? We even have an automated renewal telephone line. Or you can just drop the videos off at any library branch, at any time—24/7.	
Patron:		I brought them back a while ago, but they weren't overdue. We had them just three weeks, like the books we took out.
Staff member:	Three weeks! But that explains everything. You see, DVDs are only loaned out for one week. And the fines are a dollar per day. Now I understand. Would you like to pay it now? You can pay by credit card, or by phone or by mail. However you prefer.	
Patron:		A dollar a day! That's impossible! That's not what I was told when I got the card two months ago! (to the interpreter) This lady is a stinking heap of old fish. What does she think, we're rich? They're just out to screw foreigners because they think we're stupid.

Role play B: The angry patient

Nurse:	Okay, the tubal ligation went well, so you can go home now. You do have someone to drive you home, right?	
Patient:		My husband will come, yes.
Nurse:	Good. Now the doctor's given you two prescriptions, the Lortab, you take one tablet every four to six hours for pain. And the Motrin 900 mg. Take that every eight hours or so when you need to for the pain. All right?	
Patient:		Yes, yes.
Nurse:	And you don't have any allergies to medication, correct?	
Patient:		No, I've never had anything like that.
Nurse:	Now, this is important. You need to make sure to keep your dressing clean. Keep the bandage clean, all right? And no baths for a week, just showers. And after the shower, put sterile bandages on. Leave the bandage on until you come back and see the doctor next week. And watch for signs of infection, if you see anything, like pus or discolored drainage just call us, we'll get you seen right away.	
Patient:		What if I see something at night?
Nurse:	Don't worry, here's the number for the ER advice nurse. Now if you're having a lot of discomfort, you can use ice packs every one to two hours if you want. Just put the ice pack over the dressing for 20 minutes. For the first few days you might have some pain around the incision. Or you could feel some nausea or shoulder pain or gas. But mostly that will go away in a few days, so it's nothing to worry about. Sometimes you can get a sore throat, so if that happens just gargle mouthwash, or you can take some over-the-counter lozenges.	
Patient:		What's that?

Nurse:	You can ask at the pharmacy. I think most people use Chloraseptic. But if you get a lot of swelling around your abdomen, or you get a fever higher than 101, or you see any drainage or pus around the incision, please call us.	
Patient:		All right. What can I eat?
Nurse:	Pretty much whatever you want as soon as you feel like your stomach can tolerate it. But right now, try to drink as much liquid as possible, especially water. And avoid alcohol as long as you're taking the pain medication. And try to eat lots of fruits and vegetables and whole grains so you don't get constipated.	
Patient:		Sure, that's fine.
Nurse:	Now, here's the important part. We want you to get up and walk around by tonight, but don't lift anything more than 10 pounds for a week. And don't drive for three to four days.	
Patient:		Don't drive! But how am I going to get to work? I only took today off.
Nurse:	Most people don't go back to work for four to seven days. Didn't they tell you?	
Patient:		No! Or maybe they did, but I didn't have an interpreter.
Nurse:	And you can't operate any kind of heavy equipment or machinery.	
Patient:		But—but that's what I do! And you mean, I really can't drive?
Nurse:	No.	
Patient:		But I work the night shift. Can't I just go home and rest and go to work?
Nurse:	No. What kind of work do you do?	
Patient:		I work in a grocery warehouse, so we do lifting and moving things all night.

Nurse:	No, you can't do that. You don't want to separate your incision, and besides, with the medication you're on, if you drive the police could pull you over and give you a citation. It would be a DUI.[29]	
	[INTERPRETER SHOULD REQUEST CLARIFICATION OF "DUI"—remind the interpreter, if necessary.]	
Patient:		Oh, that sounds bad.
Nurse:	Driving under the influence means like driving drunk, or on drugs, except in your case it's legal medication.	
Patient:		And then what happens?
Nurse:	If the police catch you, they give you a ticket. You have to pay a fine, and it's a black mark on your driving record so your driving insurance rates could go up. (voice grows more gentle) But there's something more important than all that. You could cause an accident. You could get hurt, or someone else could get hurt. Maybe even kids.	
Patient:		But I don't understand why I can't drive. I feel fine, really. I just won't take the pain medicine.
Nurse:	First, you may want the pain meds! Even if you don't take them, we gave you medication to sedate you for the tubal ligation. And that's going to stay in your system for probably 12 hours. So you may think you're fine, but your body knows better. It can't react quickly enough to drive tonight. That's why it's not safe. And anyway you can't do your job.	
Patient:		But I'll get fired. You don't understand.
Nurse:	I just mean—	
Patient:		This nurse is out of her mind, she thinks I can just lie around waiting to get better, that's crazy. I have a family to protect, I can't listen to this nonsense any more. No one told me, I had no idea. I never would have done this if I knew I was going to be off work for a week, they can't do this to me!

---

[29]DUI (driving under the influence) refers to the act or crime of driving while the driver is affected by alcohol or drugs (prescription medication or illegal drugs).

Questions *after* viewing the self-recorded video of the role play selected

1. Did the interpreter, when mediating, behave differently or say something different when speaking to the librarian/nurse than when speaking to the library patron/patient? If so, how? Why do you think that happened?

_____

_____

_____

2. Examine the body language of the interpreter. How did it look the same, or different, when mediating vs. while interpreting?

_____

_____

_____

3. Examine the body language of the interpreter while mediating with the librarian/nurse vs. the library patron/patient: was the body language noticeably different? How? If so, why do you think it was different?

_____

_____

_____

4. If time permits, repeat the exercise with another interpreter and perhaps the other role play (except for medical interpreters, who should use Role Play B again). Then revisit the three questions above again and note any differences.

_____

_____

_____

_____

_____

_____

Learning Objective 3.5

After completing this section and its corresponding exercises, the learner will be able to:
- Define cultural competence and demonstrate three strategies for performing strategic cultural mediation.

 Learning Activity 3.5(a): Introduction to Cultural Mediation: A Role Play

Instructions

- In groups of three, act out the role play below.
- *Do not let the interpreter see the script.*
- When those playing the pediatrician and the nurse reach the end of the script, act out spontaneously for a little longer based on however the interpreter responds to the situation.
- Afterwards, discuss how the interpreter handled the situation and whether you agree.

Cultural mediation role play: The evil eye

Pediatrician:	Well, I think your baby has a touch of jaundice, but apart from that he seems to be doing well.	
Mother:		But I don't think that's the problem.
Pediatrician:	You think there's another problem? What is it?	
Mother:		My neighbor.
Pediatrician:	Your neighbor? What does your neighbor have to do with it?	
Mother:		She looked at him all funny.
Pediatrician:	I don't understand. How does that affect your baby's health?	
Mother:		Ever since then he doesn't sleep right. And he cries a lot. And he doesn't eat as much.
Pediatrician:	Well, actually he's put on weight since our last visit and he's right at the 75th percentile for weight and height. I'd say he's doing pretty well.	

Mother:		No, I'm worried about him, worried sick.
Pediatrician:	But why are you so worried?	
Mother:		It's the evil eye. That's what she did.
Pediatrician:	Pardon?	
Mother:		(whispers to the interpreter), YOU understand. You can explain. You know our culture. It's the evil eye.
Pediatrician:	Interpreter, can you just tell me what's going on here? What does she mean by the "evil eye"?	

 Learning Activity 3.5(b): Defining Culture

Instructions

- Ahead of time, if possible, let everyone in the class who can do so bring a small object that carries personal cultural significance.
- Let the class gather in a circle inside the room.
- All those who feel comfortable doing so should close their eyes.
- Pass your object to the person on your right.
- Guess what object is in your hand and also what you think its cultural significance might be to the person who handed it to you.
- If and when instructed to do so, state your guess out loud.
- Now, as a group, discuss what you think culture is.

Learning Activity 3.5(c): Defining Cultural Competence

Instructions

- In pairs or small groups, read the definitions of cultural competence below.
- Decide which definition your group likes best.
- Be prepared to justify your selection.

Sample definitions of cultural competence

A set of attitudes, skills, behaviors, and policies that enable organizations and staff to work effectively in cross-cultural situations.

—Cross, Bazron, Dennis, & Isaacs (1989)[30]

The ability by health care providers and health care organizations to understand and respond effectively to the cultural and linguistic needs brought by patients to the health care encounter.

—U.S. Department of Health and Human Services Office of Minority Health[31]

Cultural competence refers to a set of academic and interpersonal skills that allow individuals to increase their understanding and appreciation of cultural differences and similarities within, among, and between groups. This requires a willingness and ability to draw on community-based values, traditions, and customs and to work with knowledgeable persons of and from the community in developing targeted interventions, communications, and other supports.

—U.S. Substance Abuse and Mental Health Services Administration[32]

The knowledge and interpersonal skills that allow providers to understand, appreciate, and work with individuals from cultures other than their own. It involves an awareness and acceptance of cultural differences; self-awareness; knowledge of the patient's culture; and adaptation of skills.

—American Medical Association[33]

Delivering Culturally Effective Care to Adolescents

The ability of individuals and systems to respond respectfully and effectively to people of all cultures, classes, races, ethnic backgrounds, sexual orientations and faiths or religions in a manner that recognizes, affirms, and values the worth of individuals, families, tribes, and communities, and protects and preserves the dignity of each.

—Child Welfare League of America[34]

---

[30]Cross, T., Bazron, B., Dennis, K., & Isaacs, M. (1989). Towards a culturally competent system of care, Volume I. Washington, District of Columbia: Georgetown University Child Development Center, CASSP (Child and Adolescent Service System Program) Technical Assistance Center.
[31]http://www.ahrq.gov/professionals/systems/primary-care/cultural-competence-mco/cultcompdef.html
[32]https://www.ctclearinghouse.org/Topics/topic.asp?TopicID=28
[33]http://www.healthequityks.org/cultural_competency.html
[34]http://66.227.70.18/programs/culturalcompetence/culturalabout.htm

Learning Objective 3.6

After completing this section and its corresponding exercises, the learner will be able to:

- Develop techniques to perform effective, culturally responsive mediation.

 Learning Activity 3.6(a): The Cultural Concern

Instructions

- In groups of three, act out the role play below.
- *Do not let the interpreter see the script.*
- However, let one of the other participants in the role play read out the first two paragraphs before the role play to the interpreter.
- When those playing the service provider and the patient/service user reach the end of the script, let the interpreter decide whether or not to perform cultural mediation.
- Afterward, discuss how the interpreter handled the situation and whether you agree.

Text to read out loud to the interpreter

The patient/service user is currently experiencing domestic violence. She is dressed in the traditional dress of her country, and she does not make eye contact with men. You, as the interpreter, are quite sure from her dress and her behavior that she probably adheres to traditional practices and therefore may feel very uncomfortable speaking to a male health professional or service provider.

Note: A woman may play the role of the provider: simply pretend that the provider is male.

Provider: Good morning, Mrs. Abdelrahman. I'm very happy you could come in. (*Interpreter interprets but Mrs. Abdelrahman does not speak or meet the provider's eyes.*)

Provider (*gentle, friendly voice*) Mrs. Abdelrahman, I'd just like to ask you a few questions and take down your story before we refer you out for services. Not just healthcare. We'd like to refer you to a domestic violence shelter and legal services that can help you self-petition for legal status in the country independently of your husband. Would you be interested?

(*Mrs. Abdelrahman still does not speak or meet the eyes of the provider.*)

Provider: Mrs. Abdelrahman, we're very worried about you. We really want to help you.

(*Mrs. Abderrahman remains silent.*)

Provider (*sounding urgent*) Is there a problem? Are you okay? (*When the woman doesn't answer the counselor turns to the <u>interpreter</u> and asks:*) Can you tell me what's going on here?

Let the interpreter handle this situation. Act out the role play to a natural conclusion based on how the interpreter responds.

Instructions (Part A)

- In pairs or small groups read the dialogues below. Each one represents an inappropriate mediation with a component of cultural and/or class bias.
- Discuss what you see wrong with the mediation.
- Write down what you would say instead.

1. "Excuse me, as the interpreter, could I ask you to use simpler language? The client doesn't understand you too well because she's not very educated."
"Excuse me, as the interpreter, I just asked the provider to clarify something."

2. When the nurse asks the patient, "So what have you been doing for your diarrhea and stomach pain?" the patient answers, "I've been seeing the folk doctor." The interpreter explains to the doctor who a folk doctor is.

3. You are interpreting for a doctor who informs the patient his blood pressure is high. But you are aware that in the culture of the patient there are many big misunderstandings about what blood pressure really means and how it affects the patient. You tell the doctor the different things that blood pressure could mean to the patient.

4. An older woman who has just had surgery is told at the hospital to drink a lot of liquids, but healthcare staff only offer her cold liquids. You are aware that, in the culture of the patient a common belief is that to drink cold liquids after surgery could cause more illness while hot liquids could help healing. So far, the patient has refused to drink anything at all but hasn't explained why, and the clinical staff are worried about her. You are too, so you share this cultural belief about hot and cold liquids with the staff.

5. You interpret for a patient sharing a hospital room with someone who has the television turned on. The patient is very agitated by the TV but is unable to say why. The provider is frustrated. You think you know the problem: this is a religiously conservative man and the images of women in scanty clothing on TV are upsetting him. So you mention this possibility to the provider.

Instructions (Part B)

- It is very important for you to practice developing your own scripts in your own authentic voice. None of the examples that follow the situations below express your natural voice.
- In pairs or small groups select at least three of the situations below. Medical interpreters should select situations 1, 4 and 7. (Some of these situations were explored earlier in this workbook, but now you will write your own scripts.)
- For purposes of this exercise, assume that you would perform a cultural mediation in each, even if in real life you would choose to continue interpreting without mediating.
- Write down what you would say if you were the interpreter intervening to perform strategic mediation.

Situation 1

The patient is an older female dressed in religiously conservative clothing. The gynecologist is male. You are aware from her clothing and demeanor that she seems very uncomfortable and isn't responding except in monosyllables to the doctor's questions. The doctor is growing frustrated. You are fairly sure this patient wants a female provider. What will you say?

Situation 2

The client is applying for subsidized housing because he was told to do so. You soon realize he has no concept of what subsidized housing is, so everything the clerk at the government agency says is confusing him. But the clerk never explains: he simply assumes that the client knows how subsidized housing works. What will you say?

Situation 3

A mother and father are meeting with a teacher. The teacher mentions the child is behind his grade level in reading. You have interpreted this accurately, but it is clear to you that the parents have no idea what "grade level" in reading means, probably because in their village there were no separate grades. Everyone of all ages went to the same little school, and students progressed at their own speed. The teacher doesn't notice this cultural misunderstanding. What will you say?

Situation 4

The doctor asked what medicine the patient was taking. She said tea, but you are culturally aware that she almost certainly means a herbal remedy. Such a remedy, if she is taking one, might cause a problematic reaction with her medication. What will you say?

Situation 5

The client is a refugee applying for his social services benefits. When they ask him about his wife, he says he has two. When they keep asking him if both are *legally* his wife, he just repeats they are both his wives. The two go back and forth. Communication breaks down and the income support specialist is upset. But you are aware that in the client's culture, sometimes "wife" is a word you use to honor the mother of your child, even if the woman is not legally your wife. What will you say?

Situation 6

The client is applying for a driver's license and is asked to submit his birth certificate as proof of identity. He refuses, but doesn't say why. The clerk informs the client that he cannot get a driver's license without this document. You interpret for a small community where the elders have stated that birth certificates must not be given to anyone outside their culture, perhaps due to lack of trust because recently a motor vehicle office confiscated the vital documents of an undocumented (illegal) resident. There is a total breakdown in communication. If you do nothing, the client won't get a driver's license, which he urgently needs to keep his job. What will you say?

Situation 7

A nutritionist is giving advice to a patient with gallbladder disease about a patient's diet, but the diet plan in no way corresponds to the traditional foods this patient eats. The patient is visibly upset about the diet but the nutritionist seems oblivious, even when the patient makes clear that the diet primarily describes food she doesn't eat. You feel compelled to point out something to the nutritionist because you fear that otherwise the patient will ignore the diet altogether and eat foods that could increase her pain and have a negative impact on her health.

Examples of things you might say when intervening to address a cultural misunderstanding. (Note: Remember, *always* interpret or report your mediations to the other party!)

Example 1: Excuse me, as the interpreter I'm concerned that what I'm interpreting about [cultural issue X] isn't clear.

Example 2: Excuse me, as the interpreter I sense a break in communication about [cultural issue Y].

Example 3: Excuse me, as the interpreter I sense a cultural misunderstanding about [Z].

Example 4: Excuse me, as the interpreter I'd like to mention that ["heart" or "report card" or "high blood pressure" or "food assistance"] can have a different meaning in the client's culture than in [English]."

Example 5: Excuse me, as the interpreter I sense some cultural unease that may be related to the provider's gender.

Other examples
- Is there some cultural concern you'd like to share with [the provider or client/patient]?
- Perhaps you'd like to ask the [client/patient or provider] about [cultural issue ABC].
- You may wish to ask the [provider or client/patient] what [cultural term XYZ] means.
- Perhaps you'd like to explore [such-and-such a cultural issue] with the [client/patient or provider].
- Maybe if you explain [the cultural issue or term], I can interpret it more clearly.

Instructions

- In groups of three, act out the following role plays, as many as you have time for, being careful to read the instructions for each specific role play.
- Let a different person play the interpreter for each role play.
- As usual the interpreter *must not look at the script.* But if you play the patient/client or the provider, be sure to sure the cultural information that precedes a role play with the interpreter by reading it out loud to him or her.
- After each role play, discuss the cultural issues, how the interpreter handled the situation and whether you think the interpreter should, or should not, intervene for any of the cultural issues in these role plays.
- If you do think the interpreter should intervene, discuss what to do and what to say when performing a targeted, non-intrusive cultural mediation.

Cultural mediation role play #1: The patient with HIV

Note: Tell the interpreter this information before acting out the role play.

Cultural issues to consider

You, the interpreter, possess the following cultural knowledge about the patient's country:

- **Daris:** Many patients would go to a traditional healer for a major illness. Some of these healers are called daris.
- **The Ladu belief:** The Ladu is a tribe. If someone in that tribe says "What is will be. And what will be, was," this is a cultural saying that means the person saying it has a possible plan to commit a violent act against someone else.

Nurse-practitioner:	Can you tell me if you've been taking your ARV medications regularly?	
Patient:		Um. Sometimes, yes.
Nurse-practitioner:	But not regularly? Have you been following the exact dosages in your treatment plan and taking them after food?	
Patient:		Maybe.
Nurse-practitioner:	I'm sorry. I'm confused. Yes or no, have you been taking the medication as your doctor prescribed it?	

Patient:		It depends on the day. The dari said not to take it on fasting day.
Nurse-practitioner:	The dari? Who is the dari?	
Patient:		It doesn't matter who they are.
Nurse-practitioner:	So you've been taking the medication but not regularly, is that right?	
Patient:		It doesn't matter.
Nurse-practitioner:	It does matter. It matters terribly. You see, this kind of medication is very important. It can keep you alive for years, maybe decades, because it can prevent your HIV infection from turning into AIDS. But you have to take the medication regularly. And you have to take your ARV medication exactly as prescribed or it won't work well.	
Patient:		I don't care about that. I care about that monster who gave me this disease. In my tribe, the Ladu, we say, "What is will be. And what will be, was."

Cultural mediation role play #2: The nutritionist

Note: Tell the interpreter this information before acting out the role play.

Cultural issues to consider

- As the interpreter you are aware (as discussed earlier in this chapter) that often patients are prescribed diets that make no real sense for patients who eat traditional foods from their own cultures. In this role play, a cultural misunderstanding takes place because the nutritionist doesn't understand this problem.

Nutritionist:	Good morning, Mrs. Wang, I'm Sonia Elkins, and I'm the nutritionist here. Do you know what we're here to talk about today?	
Patient:		Yes, they told me I have diabetes. I have to eat different somehow. I'm not sure how.

Nutritionist:	And I'm going to help you do that. First I just want to explain something important. Whenever you eat your body breaks food down into glucose, which is a simple sugar. That glucose goes into your blood. But your blood needs to be at the right level. Insulin is a hormone that helps us keep our blood sugar at that ideal level. The problem with diabetes is that your body can't respond to insulin very well, so you may get high blood sugar levels, and that's bad for your health. Are you with me so far?	
Patient:		(hesitant, clearly unsure) Uh. I guess so.
Nutritionist:	If your blood sugar stays too high, it raises your risk of heart disease, stroke, kidney disease, nerve problems and problems with your feet. So this is really, really important.	
Patient:		OK.
Nutritionist:	Now, the kinds of foods you eat can make this problem better or worse. My job is to help you feel better and improve your health. If you do what I tell you you'll probably feel the difference pretty quickly—I'd say in about a week.	
Patient:		But the doctor said I have to test my blood? How am I going to test my blood? I'm so confused.
Nutritionist:	There's a nurse here, and don't worry, she's going to walk you through all of that. Honestly, these days testing your blood sugar level is pretty easy, you're lucky. You'll be surprised how easy and simple it is. But right now I want to talk about what you eat, okay?	
Patient:		OK.

Nutritionist:	Now, the form you filled out for me mentions a lot of noodles and rice and rice soup. I'm sorry, but we need you to cut back on all that. All right?	
Patient:		Oh.
Nutritionist:	The fruit and vegetables and fish are fine, but I heard there's a lot of sugar in the dishes they cook in your culture, right?	
Patient:		Uh, I guess so.
Nutritionist:	So you need to eat very, very little food with sugar in it. Here's a list of what you can eat. Please eat the foods from this list and cut back on butter and fat. Try to eat three small to moderate meals a day and if you have snacks try and shoot for the healthy snacks like milk and an apple or a banana.	
Patient:		Oh.
Nutritionist:	I see in your form here that you're walking every day. That's great. Keep it up.	
Patient:		(crying) But if I can't eat noodles and rice and rice soup—what can I eat?
Nutritionist:	I told you. You can eat anything on this list.	
Patient:		But that's not my food.
Nutritionist:	I know a lot of people find it hard to make the transition to a diabetic diet, but then they get used to it.	
Patient:		But it's not my food.
Nutritionist:	Well, give it a shot and see what happens. Let's set you up with an appointment in four weeks and we'll see how you're doing then, okay?	

Cultural mediation role play #3: The sexual assault center

Note: Tell the interpreter this information before acting out the role play.

Cultural issues to consider

You, the interpreter, possess the following cultural knowledge about the patient's country:

- The cultural expression "the cloud is getting low on the horizon," usually means that someone is so depressed he or she wants to die.
- In this culture, sexual matters in general but sexual assault in particular are rarely discussed outside the family because of the intense shame and stigma attached to sexual assault.

Office manager:	Good morning, Mrs. Bena. What can I do for you? The receptionist said you wanted to speak to someone in charge.	
Mother:		Hi. I'm—I'm not sure if this is the right place. And I wanted to speak in a private office, not the waiting room. (Lowers voice) It's about my daughter.
Office manager:	We're the county sexual assault center. Is that why you've come to us about your daughter?	
Mother:		Well, we had to flee my country because my husband was arrested and sent to prison. And while we were living in the refugee camp—I hate to say this...
Office manager:	Someone hurt your daughter?	
Mother:		Yes.
Office manager:	How old was she?	
Mother:		Thirteen.
Office manager:	(very gentle voice) I'm so sorry to hear this, Mrs. Bena. Do you feel comfortable sharing what happened to your daughter?	

Mother:		At first she seemed fine. Very brave, but quiet. Since then—we were in the camp about six months and we've been in this country for a year now. And suddenly she's so sad and quiet, she can barely study. And she was such a wonderful student! And so cheerful and sweet and kind. And now all she wants to do is sit in her room alone and listen to music. I'm really worried about her. I'm wondering if it was—the bad things. But why would it take so long to affect her like this?
Office manager:	I want you to know is that it's not unusual to see a delayed reaction like this. In fact, some children who are assaulted don't begin to feel it for many years— even grown women. We'd be happy to see her. I think we might really be able to help her.	
Mother:		But... How would that work, exactly?
Office manager:	First, we'd like to have her come for an intake exam with a therapist to find out what she needs. Then I suspect they'll recommend individual therapy sessions, maybe once a week. I have to warn you there's a waiting list, but sometimes younger clients and more urgent cases move up the list faster. Do you know if your daughter has had any thoughts of hurting herself?	
Mother:		Sometimes she says things like the cloud is getting low on the horizon. Things like that.

Office manager:	Well, that concerns me. I'm going to give you a number to call in case she needs help right away. It's our 24-hour crisis hotline,[35] and it's completely anonymous and safe. She can say anything, she doesn't even have to give her name. And the hotline counselors will know what to do.	
Mother:		There's something I have to tell you. First, we have no money.
Office manager:	That's no problem. We have sliding scale fees. I can hook you up with someone who'll help you fill out a form and then you provide proof of income—pay stubs or last year's taxes.	
Mother:		We don't have anything like that.
Office manager:	Please don't worry. We never turn away anyone for financial reasons. So you might end up paying $10 per session or even less. Please don't worry about money.	
Mother:		The other thing is more difficult. In our culture—well—these things— you know. (turns to the interpreter) YOU tell her.
Office manager:	We know there are a lot of complicated cultural issues about sexual assault. Not just in your culture—in almost every culture. That's where you can help us, by giving us all the cultural information you can to help us with your daughter. Our therapists will try to research the culture too. But everything you can tell us can be important, because it's cultural information about your family, and we'll be happy to listen.	
Mother:		Thank you. I only want to see my daughter happy again. That's all that matters to me.

[35]A hotline is a free service that provides telephone crisis intervention counseling offered by professional or trained volunteer counselors. Hotlines are especially common for specific topics such as suicide, domestic violence, youth crisis or sexual assault.

Cultural mediation role play #4: My heart hurts

Note: Tell the interpreter this information before acting out the role play.

Cultural issues to consider

You, the interpreter, possess the following cultural knowledge about the patient's country:
- "My heart hurts" means "I am very sad," usually with reference to some family matter.

Nurse:	Mrs. Galina, what's wrong, why did you press the buzzer? You look so sad!	
Patient:		My heart is hurting.
Nurse:	Oh, I'm sorry to hear that. How long has it been hurting?	
Patient:		All day.
Nurse:	Goodness, Mrs. Galina, it's 10 p.m.! Why didn't you tell us? Never mind, how bad is the pain?	
Patient:		Very bad. So bad.
Nurse:	Where is it located?	
Patient:		Right here. In my heart.
Nurse:	Would you say it feels like tightness? Or heavy pressure? Or squeezing? Or crushing pain?	
Patient:		No, no, it just hurts.
Nurse:	So you don't have any pain in your arm or your back? Or your jaw? Or your neck or shoulder?	
Patient:		No.
Nurse:	Hmm. I don't see angina in your chart here, but I'm just wondering about that. Have you been experiencing any fatigue or shortness of breath?	
Patient:		No, not at all.
Nurse:	And no nausea or heartburn?	
Patient:		No, it's just my heart. My heart hurts.

Nurse:	Oh, dear, I don't know if you need nitroglycerine or what's going on. I don't work this floor, so I don't really know. Let me call Dr. Kumar right now. He's the doctor on call.	
Patient:		No, no, I don't need a doctor. I need my daughter.
Nurse:	But you said your heart is hurting.	
Patient:		My heart is hurting because it's my birthday, and my daughter did not call me.

Cultural medication role play #5: The patient with anxiety

Note: Tell the interpreter this information before acting out the role play.

Cultural issues to consider

You, the interpreter, possess the following cultural knowledge about the patient's country:

- Mental illness in general is somewhat stigmatized but in particular many people (though by no means all) feel that taking drugs for mental disorders is a sign of weakness and failure.
- In this culture, sexual matters in general but sexual assault in particular are rarely discussed outside the family because of the intense shame and stigma attached to sexual assault.
- Many people there believe that spirits can drive one mad.
- "Ants in their head" is a reference to crazy people.

THERAPIST:	It's such a pleasure to meet you today. I know this may all be new for you, but please feel free to ask me questions at any time or let me know if I'm not clear.	
PATIENT:		Thanks.
THERAPIST:	What I'd like to do today is get a sense of what brought you here. I hope you can share some of the things you're experiencing and what you think may be causing your symptoms. For example, it would be helpful if you could let me know how you feel physically, how well you're sleeping, and how you're eating.	

PATIENT:		Well, I'm having some trouble. I don't go to work anymore. I used to sleep good even during the war back home, but these days it's real tough. I used to love my food like crazy, now it tastes like birdshit. Sometimes I just sit down and cry like a sniveling brat.
THERAPIST:	I'm so glad you came in. The kinds of symptoms you're talking about are often caused by stress. It could be short-term or long-term stress, but either way I hope we can find a way to help you feel better.	
PATIENT:		So you… I thought maybe I was going crazy from spirits or something. You don't think I'm going crazy?
THERAPIST:	I definitely would like to hear more, but I also want to reassure you that everything you've described so far is pretty typical of people who are feeling stressed. Can you tell me how you feel physically?	
PATIENT:		My back hurts like hell, and it never used to.
THERAPIST:	Well, we should get you a medical exam for that, but did you know that back pain can sometimes be caused or affected by stress?	
PATIENT:		No, I didn't have a clue. We got here, like, four months ago, maybe, or—no six months—my brain is fried. But you know, now that I think about it—that's when the back pain started! It's a total pain, it wrecks me.
THERAPIST:	Have you noticed anything that might be causing you to feel stressed?	

PATIENT:		Well, to be honest, we're refugees, new arrivals. My husband's family, they had it bad. The whole clan ended up in jail or killed, and those bastards tortured his father and brothers. I hope they fry in hell. We saw his dad's body afterward. My own family, some of them kicked the bucket. Some of them starved to death. My folks escaped with us, but two cousins of mine were—well, bad stuff happened. (long pause) You know.
THERAPIST:	I'm so sorry to hear about what you and your family suffered. That sounds like a terrible burden for you to bear. I'm wondering if you might be experiencing some other distress. Have you been to a doctor?	
PATIENT:		Yeah.
THERAPIST:	Did they do tests and make sure you were physically all right?	
PATIENT:		Sure, except they said I needed some stuff like vitamins and iron.
THERAPIST:	So the doctor hasn't put you on any medication?	
PATIENT:		No.
THERAPIST:	That's good, because sometimes when people lose their energy it's because they're not sleeping well or they're stressed, but we always want to be sure there's nothing going on medically. Can you talk to me about how you're feeling with your husband and children?	
PATIENT:		Oh, my poor tykes. They're good kids, but you know, they have tons of nightmares and they miss home all the time and then they blubber. And my husband—well, he gets pissed, he says since we came to America I'm not a real woman any more.

THERAPIST:	What do you mean?	
PATIENT:		(starts to sound fidgety and awkward). Well, you know. Back home it's different
THERAPIST:	Different how?	
PATIENT:		He—he didn't want me to work or leave the house. But now I have to. We need the money. So he gets angry sometimes.
THERAPIST:	Angry? Can you give me an example?	
PATIENT:		Well, he raises his voice and… But it only happens when he hits the bottle.
THERAPIST:	And how much is he drinking?	
PATIENT:		Please. I heard if immigration hears bad stuff, they can deport you.
THERAPIST:	I won't report anything you say to immigration. I just want to be sure you're safe. Are you feeling safe right now?	
PATIENT:		(starts to cry) Well, in my country, you know, it's—it's okay to hit me, that's our religion.
THERAPIST:	You're saying he's hurt you physically?	
PATIENT:		Sometimes. But no big deal, and I swear it's the booze.
THERAPIST:	What about your children? Has he hurt them?	
PATIENT:		No, no, he's a good guy, it's just from all that shit he went through during the war. And he's hurting bad. His dad is six feet under, his brothers are dead as doornails. So he drinks.

THERAPIST:	I am so glad you're sharing this, thank you. It's so important. You're giving me a better understanding about everything you and family are dealing with, and it's clearly very difficult and painful for all of you. Now, I just want to be absolutely certain. Can you tell me if you're feeling safe at home?	
PATIENT:		Oh yes, I told you, it's just the booze, especially the hard stuff.
THERAPIST:	I do think we can help you. We provide therapy, individual and family and group therapy. We can talk about all that, but first I just wanted to mention that for people who are going through what you do, sometimes trying medication for a period of time can be helpful too.	
PATIENT:		You mean drugs for the head? NO WAY.
THERAPIST:	What exactly are your concerns?	
PATIENT:		(begins to cry again) That's for crazy people. I'm not crazy. I won't pop pills.
THERAPIST:	Just to be clear, I don't think you're crazy. Really I don't.	
PATIENT:		You don't know what happened to me. If you knew what happened to me in prison, you'd think I was off my rocker.
THERAPIST:	You were in prison?	
PATIENT:		Yes. For three months. But what happened there… We say in my country, they threw me to the spirits. It means… Well, I don't know how to explain it.
THERAPIST:	Can you talk to me more about the spirits?	
PATIENT:		No. Because they came to me when the soldiers… Two soldiers came every day. No, I can't talk about stuff. It's not—I can't.

THERAPIST:	But it sounds like you may have been hurt. And when people get badly hurt, it can affect their minds because our minds are connected to your bodies. Let me explain. If you ever hurt your back, it means you can be at risk for back injuries, so you have to take care of your back injury. Otherwise it could get worse. And depression and stress can be like that too. If we can reduce the pain before it gets too bad—medication can help with that—it can reduce the chance of having another major problem with depression. And that can help you feel safe to work through what happened to you. So it might be a good idea to treat your symptoms as soon as you can.	
PATIENT:		But in my country, if somebody is depressed or they take drugs for the head…
THERAPIST:	Then what?	
PATIENT:		We call them bad names. Like, so-and-so, they got ants in their head.
THERAPIST:	I hope you don't believe I think you're crazy. I really don't. We'll do everything we can to help you, and no one here will think you're crazy.	
PATIENT:		Even if I saw things in prison that—I mean—things that weren't even there?
THERAPIST:	That's certainly something you can bring up in therapy. Sometimes the mind has special ways of protecting itself when terrible things happen. But it sounds like you're having a difficult time with stress and maybe depression, and that happens to many people. It doesn't make you crazy. I hope you'll think about the medication.	

LEARNING OBJECTIVES

After completing this chapter and its corresponding exercises, the learner will be able to:

OBJECTIVE 4.1

Professional Identity and the Community Interpreter
Explore professional identity for interpreters as individuals and as representatives of the profession.

OBJECTIVE 4.2

Professional Practice
Understand the business practices and legal obligations of community interpreters.

OBJECTIVE 4.3

Legal Interpreting
Explore how community interpreters can perform effective legal interpreting in community settings.

OBJECTIVE 4.4

Emerging Specializations
Identify and explore common areas of specialization within community interpreting.

OBJECTIVE 4.5

Preparing Terminology
Develop strategies and techniques to acquire specialized subject matter knowledge and terminology in community interpreting.

OBJECTIVE 4.6

Remote Interpreting
Discuss the history and challenges of remote interpreting.

Learning Objective 4.1

After completing this section and its corresponding exercises, the learner will be able to:

- Explore professional identity for interpreters as individuals and as representatives of the profession.

 Learning Activity 4.1(a): Professional or Unprofessional?

Instructions

- Read Section 4.1 of *The Community Interpreter®: An International Textbook* (pp. 274-289) on professional identity.
- Answer the questions below

1. In your own words, what is "professional identity"?

_____

_____

_____

_____

2. Why is "professional identity" important for community or medical interpreters?

_____

_____

_____

_____

3. In your own words, define what "professional" and "unprofessional" mean to you.

_____

_____

_____

_____

4. After reading this section, do you consider yourself a professional interpreter? Why?

_____

_____

_____

_____

5. In order to become a truly professional community, or medical, interpreter, what exactly do you need to do?

_____

_____

_____

_____

 Learning Activity 4.1(b): The Elements of Your Image

Instructions

- Break into teams of three to four participants.
- Discuss the elements of individual and collective professional identity within your team.
- Discuss what you, as an interpreter, already do to project this professional image (if you are a practicing interpreter) and whatever else you could do to show the world that you are a professional interpreter.
- Write these in two columns on easel chart paper and post your paper on a wall.

Learning Objective 4.2

After completing this section and its corresponding exercises, the learner will be able to:
- Understand the business practices and legal obligations of community interpreters.

 Learning Activity 4.2(a): Comparing Employed vs. Self-Employed Interpreters

Instructions

- Study the three tables below, which are from *The Community Interpreter®: An International Textbook* .
- Answer the questions that follow the tables.
- The class will divide into two debate teams, each with two appointed spokespersons: one team to proclaim, in debate, the benefits of being a self-employed interpreter and another to proclaim the benefits of being an employed interpreter.
- The class will divide in half, one half for each spokesperson or debate team. Choose which half to go to.
- Using comments from the answers to your questions below, give your spokesperson or debate team your ideas for the debate.
- Your instructor will convene the debate between the spokespersons or teams.
- You might be permitted to feed some ideas to your spokespersons during the debate itself, at the discretion of your instructor.

Note: Two of the following tables are taken from Chapter 4 of *The Community Interpreter®: An International Textbook.* They give you an overview of the differences between an employee and a self-employed contractor. While the distinctions in these three tables apply specifically to the United States in particular, similar distinctions exist in many and perhaps most countries.

Employee	Self-employed
Submits timesheets or other form of regular reporting	Submits an invoice (weekly, per project, etc)
Qualifies for benefit coverage (such as paid leave, dental care, retirement plans or other benefits, depending on the country and business)	Does not qualify for benefits
Has taxes deducted from paychecks	Is usually responsible for own tax payments, including self-employment taxes (where applicable)
Follows instructions about when, where and how to work	Is free to work when and for whom she wants
Receives a salary or wages	Is paid by the job based on invoice
Often has steady, secure income	Carries the risk of profit or loss
Works only for one company	Usually works for several organizations
May be trained by the employer to perform services in a particular manner	Should be knowledgeable about the professional protocols and best practices
Renders services personally (cannot subcontract work to someone else)	Renders services and can subcontract work
May be reimbursed for expenses (e.g., for continuing education, an interpreter badge or a bilingual dictionary)	Might or might not be compensated for direct expenses (e.g., travel or parking) but is not typically compensated for business or educational expenses (e.g., training, business cards)
Furnishes tools, equipment and materials	Is responsible for providing own material and equipment
Can be terminated or can resign	**Cannot be terminated except for breach of contract, but might lose a contract renewal (i.e., might never be asked back to interpret).**

Table 4-A
Employed vs. Self-Employed: a Business Perspective

174

Self-Employed vs. Employed Interpreters

Business mindset	I need to be self-disciplined and organized. I must track my assignments and related expenses (mileage, travel time, highway tolls, etc.) and consult a qualified accountant. I need to invoice clients regularly and remind them to pay me as needed. I set my own financial goals to earn a living. I must consider getting liability and/or other insurance (e.g., errors and omissions).	I prefer the security of a fixed salary without constantly pursuing work or payment. I enjoy employee status rather than running a business. I do not want to worry about professional insurance or deal with paperwork. I am not detail oriented and prefer not to track all my expenses.
Marketing mindset	I need to promote myself to several clients. To do that, I will develop materials like a résumé, bio and a social media or website presence to show the credentials that highlight me and my services. I will distribute these materials to acquire more clients to help me get a steady income. Paying for these materials is an investment in my business and career.	I enjoy a collegiate atmosphere. I don't want to talk about myself or insert marketing into my conversations. I prefer to invest my free time and discretionary money in fun activities, not marketing materials. I can get free training, continuing education and paid career opportunities.
Flexibility and adaptability	I like to have full control of my time and decide when to work—or not. I like the idea of being my own boss. I want to turn down work that I do not like or that makes me uncomfortable. I don't like a predictable routine: I enjoy the fact that each day can be different—it's an adventure!	I like a set schedule so that I have full freedom outside my working hours. I like being able to plan ahead and enjoy a lot of activities that I can arrange around my schedule. It is fun to climb up the employment ladder and achieve success and recognition.
Open to freedom, new experiences and irregular schedule	I enjoy the ability to decide who to work for and to look for the clients who fit my goals and values. I don't feel isolated working for myself: in fact, I enjoy meeting new people all the time.	I prefer to work with only one organization where I have close ties and a sense of working with colleagues and friends. The structured work environment sets up clear expectations for me.
Vision, Mission and Values – a statement of professional culture	I am clear about who I am, what I do and my purpose as an interpreter. I send out a clear message to clients and users and develop a clear vision for my career path. I may do business research to understand what "vision," "mission" and "values" mean in business. My professional image revolves around the sum of these elements, which make up my professional culture and are reflected in my professional identity.	I prefer associating with a company that has made choices about professional culture. The company I work for has a clear vision, mission and core values. It walks its talk. When something contradicts these statements I feel comfortable bringing it up. It is important for me to work with a company whose vision, mission and values align with mine.

Table 4-B
Costs and Benefits of Being Self-employed (Freelance) vs. Employed Interpreters

Self-Employed vs. Employed Interpreters: Legal Considerations		
Documentation: complaints about "too much paperwork!" A reputable ISP is diligent about meeting its legal and fiscal requirements.	It is your job to collect and submit all required paperwork. Refuse to submit required paperwork only if it is in conflict with your professional ethics or local laws. (e.g., the ISP should not demand that you document details of the encounter that violate confidentiality.)	Employees are mandated to comply with the employer's documentation requirements, which are usually straightforward and often the employer helps you take care of it. If you object to any of it, keep a written record of your communication.
Paperwork: complaints about "I have to submit the same document again!" Keeping interpreter files updated is a sign of a healthy organization. Updates are a snapshot of the agency's status quo.	It is your responsibility and in your best interest to keep all your records up to date, such as training or workshops, new credentials like certification, yearly tests or other required documents (e.g., vaccinations, criminal record background checks) and proof of insurances.	The employer will usually require new documentation when a document on file is due to expire. You will not have to remember it yourself but must usually comply with the request.
Lack of compliance with procedures: complaints about "Why do I have to do all this!" Each ISP is legally bound to honor its signed contractual agreements. They are not doing this to you for fun!	It is your obligation to fulfill the requirements you accepted in your contract, such as: Fulfilling administrative tasks related to the assignment. Presenting appropriate invoices with all necessary information. Reporting critical incidents or concerns that the ISP should know. Declining to perform services other than those you were engaged for.	Employers should have procedures and workflows in place to ensure compliance. They should also have a policy in place for employees who violate compliance requirements.

Table 4-D
Legal Considerations for Self-Employed (Freelance) vs. Employed interpreters

Questions

1. After studying these tables, in small groups write in the lines provided what your group considers to be the three most important differences between employed vs. self-employed interpreters.

_____

_____

_____

_____

2. What, in your opinion, are the three greatest benefits of being a self-employed interpreter? What are some of the greatest costs or disadvantages?

_____

_____

_____

_____

3. What, in your opinion, are the three greatest benefits of being an employed interpreter? What are some the greatest costs or disadvantages?

_____

_____

_____

Learning Activity 4.2(b): What's In Your Business Toolbox

Instructions

- Refer to pp. 294-297 of *The Community Interpreter®: An International Textbook*.
- Select from the list below those elements that you have, or plan to have, as a professional interpreter.
- For each item that you do not select, briefly state why you do not want to include it.

Elements of your business toolbox:

Résumé: _____

Portfolio: _____

Trade name: _____

Business cards: _____

Professional email address: _____

Mobile telephone with professional voice message: _____

Business forms[36]: _____

Website or social media presence: _____

Branding statement[37]: _____

Business stationery: _____

Professional invoice forms: _____

Other (specify): _____

---

[36] The business forms you might need as an interpreter will vary by country and region and will also depend on whether you are a freelancer or an employee. Such forms could include, for example, forms required to set up a small business, comply with tax regulations or document your immigration status, among many others.

[37] A branding statement is a concise professional description of "who you are and what you do." It communicates the essence of your professional image. For example you could print on your business cards, Providing the highest-quality medical interpreting across Delaware since 1995 or Sami Bashir, the only court- and medically-certified Arabic interpreter in [your province, city or region]. See p. 297 of *The Community Interpreter®: An International Textbook* for a more detailed explanation of branding statements.

177

After completing this section and its corresponding exercises, the learner will be able to:

- Explore how community interpreters can perform effective legal interpreting in community settings.

 Learning Activity 4.3(a): Quiz: Legal Interpreting in Community Settings[37]

Legal interpreting involves interpreting for a legal process or proceeding. In many countries and perhaps most, community (including medical) interpreters and legal (especially court) interpreters follow different ethics and standards of practice for community vs. legal interpreting, and different skills are required to perform such work. It is often critically important to know if you are performing *legal interpreting in community settings.*

Instructions

- In pairs, decide whether each situation below could be considered legal interpreting (write L), general community interpreting (write C) or something in between that we shall call "quasi-legal" interpreting (write QL).
- As you do, try to consider whether each situation below is part of a legal process, *could* be (or become) part of a legal process or involves any legal documents and paperwork.
- Remember that almost any document that a service user is required to sign is typically considered a legal document.

1. ____ At a board hearing, a school superintendent hears arguments and decides whether or not to expel/suspend a student.

2. ____ A Child Protective Services investigator interviews a parent about suspected child neglect.

3. ____ A lawyer for a nonprofit legal services organization meets with a woman to discuss her divorce proceedings.

4. ____ A patient meets with a doctor about a back injury for a workers' compensation case.

5. ____ The interpreter is asked to sight translate a consent form.

6. ____ A resident from El Salvador meets an immigration counselor to fill out a Temporary Protective Status (TPS) and work permit form.

7. ____ An elderly resident applies for a government benefit.

8. ____ A police officer at the scene of an accident comforts a wife whose husband has just been taken by helicopter to a hospital. Their car was struck head on by a drunk driver.

---

[38]Adapted from Bancroft and Rubio-Fitzpatrick (2011). The Community Interpreter: A Comprehensive Training Manual, 5th ed. Columbia, MD: Culture & Language Press, pp. 84-85.

9. ____ Same situation as above, but the *husband* was the drunk driver and the police officer asks the wife questions about the accident.

10. ____ An interview where a U.S. Census Bureau surveyor asks an LEP resident census questions.

11. ____ A subsidized housing office warns a family that if too many working adults live in their house they will lose their Section-8 housing because they will no longer qualify.

12. ____ A woman goes to file a Protection Order to prevent her abusive husband from coming near her or their children.

13. ____ A restaurant worker files a discrimination complaint with a local office of human rights.

 Learning Activity 4.3(b): Legal vs. Medical Interpreting

- According to the directions from your instructor, in groups of three either act out or read together the following role play. It concerns child sexual abuse.
- Let the person playing Mr. Sanchez sight translate the text into another language, if appropriate, to allow for bidirectional interpreting.
- Answer the questions that follow the role play.

The fine line to the legal world: An unexpected home visit for sexual abuse

Case worker:	Hello Mr. Sanchez, how are you?	
Mr. Sanchez:		Good, good. How are you? But today is not Tuesday. We don't have a visit today, right?
Case worker:	No we don't. But I received a call from Rosie's school and I'm here to verify a few things. This is Mr. Reynolds, he is an officer of the Blue County Police Department and is here with me today to ask you a few questions. Can we come in?	
Mr. Sanchez:		Sure, please come in. Did something happen to Rosy?
Case worker:	They called me from school. Rosy asked the nurse to call me. Rosy seemed pretty upset. She said you tried to kiss her inappropriately.	

Mr. Sanchez:		No, this is crazy. This is a big mistake. I never tried to kiss her. Not in the way she thinks. Ms. Brooks you know that, right? You know me!
Officer:	So, what do you mean "not in the way she thinks"?	
Mr. Sanchez:		My wife always complained that I was closer to the boys than to the girl. I spend a lot of time with my sons playing basketball, taking them to the movies, but not with my daughter. She was really getting on my case, my wife I mean. She kept telling me that she is now a teenager and if I did not show her affection she would grow up thinking that her father did not love her.
Officer:	So, what happened?	
Mr. Sanchez:		As I said, my wife was on my case, so I went downstairs, she was watching TV and I hugged her… she pushed me away and yelled "what are you doing?" and ran away. Next thing I know, you are knocking at my door asking me questions about this kissing stuff.
Officer:	Why do you think she pushed you away and ran away?	
Mr. Sanchez:		I think she misunderstood my intentions because I never showed her affection. And now that I was listening to my wife, well… she had no way of knowing… but I would never do anything wrong to my daughter… she is my daughter.
Officer:	I need you to come with me to the police station. I will ask the interpreter to come with us so we can continue with these questions.	
Mr. Sanchez:		But… why?

Questions

1. As the interpreter, do you think this scenario is an example of healthcare interpreting? Social services interpreting? Legal interpreting? All three, or any of the above? Why?

_____

_____

_____

2. If ethics and standards for legal interpreters are different where you live and work than those for community interpreters, which ethics and standards would you adhere to in the situation above? Why? Give specific reasons.

_____

_____

_____

3. Would you agree to go to the police station and continue to interpret the case? Why or why not?

_____

_____

_____

4. Which qualifications, skills and knowledge would you need to interpret for law enforcement at a police station—or a home visit? Why?

_____

_____

_____

Learning Activity 4.3(c): Settlement Paperwork

Instructions

- Read the two sample worker's compensation claim and settlement forms from the state of Maryland in the United States that appear on the next pages.[39]
- Now imagine that you are assisting an injured worker who requires interpreting services at medical, rehabilitative and other appointments where such forms may be involved or signed.
- Furthermore, at the end of a particular medical session, the injured worker asks you, the interpreter, to please "have a look" at all his other settlement papers.
- Now answer the questions on the next page.

---

[39] http://www.wcc.state.md.us/adjud_claims/forms.html#settlement

WORKERS' COMPENSATION COMMISSION
SETTLEMENT WORKSHEET

Claimant: _____ Claim No.: _____

Claimant Atty.: _____ Atty. Telephone: _____

Claimant's age: _____ years, _____ months

Employer: _____

Insurer: _____

Employer/Insurer Atty.: _____

This worksheet has been prepared by Claimant, or Claimant's attorney, for the purpose of securing the Commission's approval of the proposed Agreement of Final Compromise and Settlement.

1.	Is the claim contested as to compensability and/or causation?	☐ Yes	☐ No
2.	Are further medical treatments recommended for the injury?	☐ Yes	☐ No
3.	Is there any potential SIF liability in the case?	☐ Yes	☐ No
4.	Is the Claimant working?	☐ Yes	☐ No
5.	Does this case involve a third party claim?	☐ Yes	☐ No
	If yes, attach document required by COMAR 14.09.01.19.		
6.	Is the claim on appeal?	☐ Yes	☐ No
7.	Is a hearing on the claim pending?	☐ Yes	☐ No
	If yes, when? _____		
8.	Has Claimant applied for Social Security disability benefits?	☐ Yes	☐ No
	If yes, when (date)? _____		
9.	Is SSDI claim pending or on appeal?	☐ Yes	☐ No
10.	Date SSDI approved: _____ or ◯ N/A		
11.	Has Claimant applied for Medicare benefits?	☐ Yes	☐ No
	If yes, when (date)? _____		
12.	Is Medicare claim pending or on appeal?	☐ Yes	☐ No
13.	Date Medicare approved: _____ or ◯ N/A		
14.	Does Claimant have End State Renal Disease (ESRD)?	☐ Yes	☐ No

SETTLEMENT WORKSHEET

15. Amount of Total Proposed Settlement: $ _____

16. Total Amount of Indemnity paid to Claimant to date: $ _____

17. Has a professional evaluator identified probable future Medicare covered expenses?   ☐ Yes   ☐ No

    If yes, attach professional evaluation.

18. Has proposed Medicare Set Aside been submitted to CMS?   ☐ Yes   ☐ No

    If yes, date submitted: _____

19. Is CMS approval of the MSA pending?   ☐ Yes   ☐ No

20. Date CMS approved MSA: _____ or ◯ N/A

21. Is there a formal medical set aside allocation?   ☐ Yes   ☐ No

    If yes, state amount: $ _____

    If yes, is the MSA administered by a TPA or paid as an annuity, with no current or future reversionary interest to claimant?   ☐ Yes   ☐ No

22. Has some of the settlement been apportioned to future medicals?   ☐ Yes   ☐ No

    If yes, attach medical evaluation or opinion.

23. Date of disablement by accidental injury or occupational disease: _____

24. Are medicals being left open?   ☐ Yes   ☐ No

25. Comments:

    ┌──┐
    │   │
    │   │
    │   │
    │   │
    │   │
    └──┘

I hereby certify that the foregoing is true and accurate based on my personal knowledge, information and belief.

_____   _____

Claimant Signature   **Attorney Signature**

10 East Baltimore Street · Baltimore, Maryland 21202-1641
410-864-5100 · Email: info@wcc.state.md.us · Web: http://www.wcc.state.md.us

MD WCC Form H-07 02/23/2015

Questions

1. What will you do when the worker asks you to "have a look" at his workers' compensation settlement papers?

_____

_____

_____

2. Is reviewing or sight translating those forms at the request of the injured worker part of your job? Why or why not? If not, when might it be appropriate to do so?

_____

_____

_____

3. If you decline to review or sight translate the paperwork, what will you say to the injured worker? Will you refer him or her to anyone else?

_____

_____

_____

4. Now the injured worker mentions that he or she has a lawyer. Will that change any of your answers above? Why or why not?

_____

_____

_____

5. Now the adjuster asks you to _read_ the settlement paperwork to the injured worker while he/she quickly runs to get other documents at her desk. What would you do? Why?

_____

_____

_____

6. Your contracting agency contracts you to meet with an injured worker to _read_ the settlement paperwork in a place you can decide. Settlement paperwork will be sent to you by email and you are asked to call the injured claimant to set the appointment (place, date and time.) Would you accept? Why or why not? What would you say to the adjuster?

_____

_____

_____

Learning Objective 4.4

After completing this section and its corresponding exercises, the learner will be able to:
- Identify and explore common areas of specialization within community interpreting.

 Learning Activity 4.4: Areas of Specialization in Community Interpreting

- Your instructor will post sheets of paper on the walls around the room. Each sheet will have the title of a sub-specialization of community interpreting, such as medical, educational, social services, faith-based legal and/or refugee interpreting. (As needed, more sheets can be added beside each sub-specialization.)
- In small groups, go to each sheet, one by one, and with a marker write down what your small group believes is the greatest challenge that interpreters might encounter in that setting. ***Leave a significant amount of white space between each challenge on the sheet!***
- As needed, refer to Section 4.4 (pp. 320-338) of ***The Community Interpreter®: An International Textbook*** to assist you.
- Next, your instructor will have your group travel again to each sheet posted around the room. This time, write down *any good solution you can think of for each challenge written on the sheet* using the blank space below each challenge. (You can even answer your own challenges.)

Instructions for medical interpreters

- Your instructor will post sheets of paper on the walls around the room. Each sheet will have the title of either a sub-specialization of medical interpreting, such as obstetrics-gynecology, pediatrics, internal medicine, emergency care, oncology, surgery, intensive care, etc., or a particular topic area related to U.S. healthcare.
- In small groups, go to each sheet, one by one, and with a marker write down what your small group believes is the greatest challenge that medical interpreters might encounter in that area of specialization or the topic area. ***Leave a significant amount of white space between each challenge on the sheet!***
- Next, your instructor will have you travel again to each sheet posted around the room. This time, write down *any good solution you can think of for each challenge written on the sheet that your team did not write* using the blank space below each challenge.

After completing this section and its corresponding exercises, the learner will be able to:

- Develop strategies to acquire the specialized subject matter knowledge and terminology needed to interpret in a broad array of community settings.

 Learning Activity 4.5(a): Techniques to Prepare Terminology

Instructions

- Read Section 4.5 (pp. 339-346) of *The Community Interpreter®: An International Textbook.*
- Answer the questions below.

1. Which techniques do you think that you, as a community interpreter, should consider when you prepare the terminology for your next assignment?

_____

_____

_____

_____

2. Which three resources do you plan to purchase or procure first in order to prepare your terminology? (Give your top three priorities. For purposes of this exercise, assume that money is no object.)

_____

_____

_____

3. How would you organize the terms learned for easy handling and memorization? Where would you store them for easy access when you needed them on an assignment?

_____

_____

_____

4. What are the benefits of creating your own glossary, if any? How would you start creating your own glossary?

_____

_____

_____

5. List the resources (for your area(s) of specialization, e.g. medical) that you currently use. Now look at the terminology section of your textbook and see if you wish to change, or add to, any of your answers.

_____

_____

_____

Learning Activity 4.5(b): Strategies to Expand Terminology

Instructions

- Read Section 4.5 (pp. 339-346) of *The Community Interpreter®: An International Textbook.*
- Answer the questions below.
- Read the sample assignments that follow the question. Imagine that the information in each case is all you know about each of these upcoming assignments.
- Select the assignment topic that you are the least familiar with.
- **Medical interpreters should select Assignment 1 or 2.**
- Mentally prepare for the potential topic of this assignment.
- List the resources, strategies and techniques you would use to prepare/create/expand the terminology for this assignment.
- By using your smartphone, or other resources, list at least 10 terms with definitions in both of your languages that are relevant for the assignment you chose.

1. Which strategies and resources do you think community interpreters should consider if they wish to expand their terminology?

_____

_____

_____

2. When building a glossary, which strategies might help you increase your knowledge of relevant terminology? Give at least three specific examples.

_____

_____

_____

3. Is there any online or software tool that would help you to expand your terminology? How?

_____

_____

_____

Overview of scenarios: You have three assignments on your schedule for which you will need to prepare terminology:

Assignment 1 Assessment of motor skills for a three-year-old child.

Assignment 2 CT scan for a patient with pancreatic cancer.

Assignment 3 Home visit to a single mother with a nine-month-old baby to assess her ability to provide for her children.

Learning Objective 4.6

After completing this section and its corresponding exercises, the learner will be able to:
- Discuss the history and challenges of remote interpreting.

Learning Activity 4.6(a): An Analysis of Remote Interpreting

Instructions

- In small groups, write answers to the questions below.
- Next, your instructor will set up a simulated experience of remote interpreting for you (either over-the-phone interpreting—OPI—or video remote interpreting—VRI).

1. In your own words, write a definition of remote interpreting.

_____

_____

_____

2. Look at p. 354 of *The Community Interpreter®: An International Textbook.* The same table is reproduced for you following these questions. After studying this table, state which are the three greatest differences you see between on-site (face-to-face/in-person) interpreters and remote interpreters.

_____

_____

_____

_____

3. Which three aspects of OPI or VRI would you find the most challenging?

_____

_____

_____

4. Which type of interpreting do you think you would find hardest to perform: on-site (face-to-face/in-person) interpreting, OPI or VRI? Why?

_____

_____

_____

On-Site Interpreters vs. Remote Interpreters		
Listening Skills	The interpreter needs active listening skills to extract meaning with access to quality sound and nonverbal cues.	OPI: The interpreter needs active listening skills to extract meaning even with inferior sound without nonverbal cues. VRI: Active listening skills to extract meaning with inferior sound and limited visibility.
Consecutive Interpreting and Note-taking	Ideally the interpreter has note-taking skills but can rely more on short-term memory because it is easier to manage turn-taking and ask for repetition face to face.	The interpreter must have adequate note-taking skills to capture longer statements, numbers, medications, instructions, etc. It is harder to manage turn-taking and interventions.
Intervention and Mediation Skills	Interpreters can use their full range of verbal and nonverbal cues to indicate the parties' needs to pause or for an intervention.	OPI: The interpreter must be assertive and ask for pauses. The timing of interventions is a nuanced skill. VRI: Gestures to request a pause might not be noticed. The interpreter will need to find a viable technique for intervening.
Delivery Skills	Onsite interpreters can monitor nonverbal cues to capture, understand and convey meaning.	With reduced or no access to context and visualization, remote interpreters more fully rely on voice, breathing, inflection, pronunciation and volume to communicate clearly. They must make the best use of voice pitch, tone and volume to effectively convey meaning in the absence of visual cues.
Accents and Language Variations	Onsite interpreters are typically exposed to a limited amount of variability of accents and language variations, as they are interpreting in a limited geographic area for a finite number of immigrant communities.	Remote interpreters are exposed to a variety of accents, language variations and regionalisms, often more than onsite interpreters. Remote interpreters are virtually connected with everybody from anywhere.
Context	Onsite interpreters typically know the settings where they interpret often, including local geographic, social, cultural, legal and societal knowledge. They are aware of how local immigrant, Deaf or indigenous communities use language and are familiar with the locally represented regional variations.	Remote interpreters may lack knowledge of a service system because it is located in another country or locality. They may miss references, cues and meaning or make errors due to lack of relevant knowledge. They may need to request more clarifications and explanations.
Professional Contact	Onsite interpreters have more direct interaction with colleagues and other professionals. They may have greater opportunity for networking, debriefing difficult sessions and socializing.	The remote interpreter may work extensively from home, in call centers or in another environment where stress is high and opportunities to socialize with colleagues may be limited.
Self care	Onsite interpreters may have better access to resources for managing job stress and for implementing a self care plan.	The remote interpreter may need to develop specialized strategies for self care tailored to the job to avoid stress, burnout and vicarious trauma (see Chapter 5).
Technology	Onsite interpreters have fewer technologies available to interpret with. They should use every available tool to support their interpreting, including smart phone dictionaries and language apps.	Remote interpreters have to learn to manage multiple technological platforms, possibly including video, OPI, dedicated WiFi connections, headsets, scheduling software and website interfaces. They typically have better access to digital resources during their interpreting.

Table 4-F
On-Site Interpreters vs. Remote Interpreters: A Comparison of Skill Sets

Learning Activity 4.6(b): Comparing face-to-face, over the phone and video remote interpreting

Instructions

- Your instructor will set up a simulated experience of remote interpreting for you (either over the phone interpreting—OPI—or video remote interpreting—VRI).
- Select one of the three role plays below for your simulated experience.
- Medical interpreters should select Role Play #2.
- After the simulated experience, answer the questions below.
- Based on your simulated experience, see if you still agree on your answers to questions 2, 3 and 4 in Learning Activity 4.6(a). Note any differences between your answers above and your experience in the lines provided.

_____

_____

_____

_____

_____

_____

Role play #1 for simulated OPI experience: The emergency call

Instructions

- For the script below, decide who plays the interpreter. The interpreter will not read the script.
- Conduct the role play by phone using a two-way or three-way call. Two of the role players can be at the same location but it should be different from the interpreter's location.
- If possible, have the interpreter at a good distance or in a different room from the other two role players.
- At the end of the exercise, each player, the interpreter included, will list the challenges or difficulties faced, if any.
- Describe what would have worked differently if the interpreting had taken place either on-site or through video remote interpreting.

Police officer:	Agent Bill Sanders, here. Found female, approximately 16, in the woods around the village. Need language support.	
Emergency dispatcher:		Can you identify the language, agent?
Police officer:	I believe it's French.	

Emergency dispatcher:		One moment… You are now connected to a French interpreter, agent.
Interpreter:	(French interpreter on the line) Hello? French interpreter 54321, this is Elise.	
Police officer:	I'm agent Bill Sanders. Don't be scared. I'm here to help. I have someone on the phone to help me, OK? Can you tell me your name?	
Female:		(breathing hard, does not answer)
Police officer:	Don't worry, you're safe. Nobody's gonna hurt you now. I'm here to help. Can you grab my hand?	
Female:		(her breathing slows down a little).
Police officer:	Good, good. Got you. Slow, now. I'm gonna help you out of here.	
Female:		I'm cold. My leg… cannot move… hurts… too much… no, no…
Police officer:	Hold on… let me get you a cover	
Police officer:	(police officer's voice fades away while getting the cover – speaks in a low or muffled voice, making it hard to hear) No worry, I'm getting a cover for you. Here… wrap it around your shoulders…. Where does it hurt?	
Female:		(very soft voice, almost impossible to hear) … Are they gone? Did you see them? … they were after me… they were big… I want to go home…
Police officer:	OK, OK, we'll take you home but first we're going to get you checked out, to be sure you're all right… Do you know who they are?	

Role play #2 for simulated OPI experience: Liver enzymes (English-Spanish)

Liver specialist (hepatologist):	I'm Dr. Wu and I am a liver specialist. I understand that you were brought in tonight by ambulance, is that correct? Can you tell me what happened?		
Patient:		Mi esposo dice que estaba dormida y de repente me levanté de la cama gritando del dolor. Dice que hablaba tonterías, cosas que no tenían sentido.	My husband says that I was asleep and all of sudden I got up screaming in pain. He says that I was talking crazy and saying things that didn't make any sense.
Liver specialist (hepatologist):	What else?		
Patient:		Dice que me puse de rodillas al lado de la cama agarrándome aquí (patient grabs her stomach).	He says that I got down on my knees next to the bed and that I was grabbing myself (patient grabs her stomach).
Liver specialist (hepatologist):	Is that all that happened?		
Patient:		Pues, yo casi no me acuerdo de nada de eso. De lo único que me acuerdo es del dolor. Sentía unas punzadas aquí, unas más fuertes que otras pero nunca se me quitaron hasta ahora. También estaba bien mareada, bien, bien mareada. De eso sí me acuerdo.	Well, I hardly remember any of that. The only thing that I remember is the pain. I felt like a stabbing pain here—some were strong and others were not as strong, but the pain never went away until now. I was also dizzy, I mean really, really dizzy. I remember that too.
Liver specialist (hepatologist):	This just started all of a sudden tonight? Have you been sick lately?		
Patient:		No, no he estado enferma últimamente. Creo que tuve un resfrío hace cuatro meses, en enero.	No, I haven't been sick lately. I think I had a cold four months ago, in January.

Liver specialist (hepatologist):	These are the only medicines that you are taking: something for depression, you have an inhaler for your asthma and something for your thyroid, right? Is there anything else?		
Patient:		Sí eso es todo de lo que tomo, nada más.	That is all I am taking, nothing else.
Liver specialist (hepatologist):	You have hypothyroidism, how long have your been taking medicine for that?		
Patient:		He estado en tratamiento para la tiroides por unos cinco o seis años, casi desde que llegué a este país.	I have been seeing a doctor for my thyroid for about five or six years, almost since I came to this country.
Liver specialist (hepatologist):	Has it ever caused you any problems before? Do you have a PCP that you see for that?		
Patient:		No, nunca he tenido problemas con ninguno de mis medicamentos.	No, I have not had any problems due to my medicines.
Liver specialist (hepatologist):	Do you drink alcohol?		
Patient:		No, para nada. Soy cristiana. No tengo ningún vicio así.	No, not at all. I am Pentecostal and I don't have any kind of bad habits.
Liver specialist (hepatologist):	Have you ever been told that you have viral hepatitis, either A, B or C?		
Patient:		No, nunca.	No, never.
Liver specialist (hepatologist):	How about a fatty liver?		
Patient:		Tampoco.	No.
Liver specialist (hepatologist):	When you came in, the nurse gave you something for the pain and started IV liquids. She also did some blood tests and the results are back, which is why they called me, a liver specialist.		

Patient:		Dígame, doctor, qué es lo que tengo, ¿hay algún problema con mi hígado?	Tell me, doctor, what is the problem. Is there something wrong with my liver?
Liver specialist (hepatologist):	Yes. Your liver enzymes are very high. The normal level is between 5 and 60 and yours is 1700. I am just not sure what could explain such a spike in these numbers.		
Patient:		Yo tampoco— ¡ay! el efecto del calmante se me está pasando…	I don't know either—ay! The effect of the pain medicine is wearing off.
Liver specialist (hepatologist):	Your white blood cell count is also high, but you don't really have a fever. So I don't think you have an infection, but I am not sure yet . I think there's definitely some inflammation of the liver and that might explain the high numbers. Again, I'm not sure.		
Patient:		Pues, usted es lo que sabe…¡ay! Me siento un poco mareada otra vez.	Well, you are the one who knows…ay! I am starting to feel dizzy again.
Liver specialist (hepatologist):	Ok, I'll let the nurse know (reaches for and pushes the call button). We're going to get some more tests. I want to do a CT scan and test for hepatitis. I'm going to start IV antibiotics. I'll give you something for dizziness as well. You will have to be admitted to the hospital so we can find out what is causing this.		
Patient:		Bueno, gracias, doctor.	Ok, thank you, doctor.

Role play #3 for simulated OPI experience: The advocate and the rape victim (English only)

Advocate:	Hi, my name is Amanda Britten, I was sent by the Sexual Assault Crisis Center.	
Survivor:		Why—why are you here?
Advocate:	I'm an advocate who's called in whenever somebody has asked for a sexual assault exam. You seem a bit nervous and upset. Has anyone upset you?	
Survivor:		(confused) But—I didn't ask for an exam. The police brought me here. I didn't ask for any exam or any advocate.
Advocate:	Sure, I understand, I'm sure this is very confusing for you. It would confuse anyone. So let me explain a little about what I do here. My services start at the hospital and I'm here for your emotional support and to make sure you're as comfortable as you can be during the exam.	
Survivor:		What exam?
Advocate:	So the police didn't tell you anything about the exam?	
Survivor:		Maybe they tried, but they didn't have an interpreter. Mainly they asked questions. They had a bilingual officer, and I didn't really understand him. He doesn't speak the same as me, and his accent was real hard to understand.
Advocate:	Okay, well don't worry, I'll tell you everything you want to know about the exam in just a minute, but we also have wonderful lawyers who can help you if you want. Let's talk about that later. Right now, I can get you snacks and blankets and anything you need here at the hospital.	
Survivor:		(starts to cry very quietly and sits down on the floor and rocks herself) No. I don't need anything. I don't want anything. I just want my life back.

Advocate:	(sits down on the floor beside her) I can totally understand how coming here would make you feel. Anyone would feel upset in this situation. Do you feel safe right now?	
Survivor:		(looks up) Yes.
Advocate:	I'm glad you feel safe, and I'm glad you're able to share how you feel right now. Let's talk a little about what I can do. Basically, how it works is that my services will end either when you're admitted here or when you leave the hospital, but I can also give you a ride to wherever you need to go. And if you need a safe place to stay, I can find a way to work on that while you are here. And then you can call me or see me at the office if you want.	
Survivor:		No, no. (chokes.) I just want to go home.
Advocate:	Sure, sure. And if you leave today and you don't want to talk to me again that's fine too. I'm here for whatever you need.	
Survivor:		No, you are very nice. I'm not mad at you.
Advocate:	Okay, I'm glad to hear that. Because we also have follow-up services, so you can still see me if you want. I'll check in once a week or so if that's okay with you, and I can get you help with therapy or housing. Did you know there's a crime survivor compensation program?	
Survivor:		What's that?
Advocate:	It's a fund of money to help crime victims with the costs. So for example, right now you have to give up your clothes for evidence—	
Survivor:		(cries) What are you saying? You mean, I lose my blouse? My mother gave me that blouse. My mother is dead. And they're going to take it away from me forever?

Advocate:	(gentle voice) I'm so sorry to hear that. I know money can't buy another blouse that your mother gave you. But the crime victims fund can give you money to compensate for any clothes that are given up for evidence, and any other costs related to the assault. Like, if you had to move, there are funds for moving. Or if you don't have health insurance, your medical bills can be covered by the crime victims compensation program. And I can work as a kind of liaison between them and you to make everything easier.	
Survivor:		Yes, please. But what about the police? I don't think they understand me.
Advocate:	If you need any kind of legal help, like a criminal protection order or help with your case, there are lawyers in my office who can help with that. And they are crime victim's rights lawyers, so this is what they do. They represent you and make sure you know your rights, and during a criminal case they're really there for you. The government will have a lawyer for you too, but those lawyers work for the government and their job is to prosecute your crime, so it's not exactly the same thing as what we provide. So if you're interested in having someone who is a lawyer who is fully present for you, that is an option. They work free of cost, so you wouldn't have to worry about that.	
Survivor:		I understand. But this exam, you said you'd tell me something about it.
Advocate:	Okay, sure. The exam will take anywhere from about two to four hours and it will start with an interview. The nurse is going to ask you about your past medical history. And just to get an idea to make sure there's nothing else we need to treat while we're here today, she'll have some questions about your sexual health and other partners you may have had. She needs to know if there's somebody else's DNA on your body because she's collecting evidence. She needs to be aware of a lot of things and you'll have to be patient with the nurse because she writes down what you say word for word because it's very important that we have your own words. It may go to court in an official court record.	

Survivor:		But the exam. What are they going to check?
Advocate:	Well, first they do a head-to-toe exam. The nurse will just check for scrapes or bruises or abrasions that you may not be aware of, that came before the assault or during the assault. And if it's okay with you, she'll take pictures of them. And after that she'll collect DNA.	
Survivor:		How? I don't understand.
Advocate:	Well, she uses kind of like a big cotton swab and she brushes it over various parts of the body that may have come in contact with your assault. And she rubs it on a slide that gets sent to the crime lab. And if there's any part of the exam you're not comfortable with you can just say so and the nurse won't do it.	
Survivor:		Really?
Advocate:	Absolutely. It's your choice. And then there's a vaginal exam, it's kind of like an OB-GYN exam. And then they'll check inside you and also do some swabs there to collect any DNA that might be inside you. And after that the nurse will be finished and she'll give you some medications that might be best for you given the assault that occurred.	
Survivor:		And then I can go home?
Advocate:	Yes! And I can drive you if you want.	

LEARNING OBJECTIVES

After completing this chapter and its corresponding exercises, the learner will be able to:

OBJECTIVE 5.1

Communicative Autonomy and the Role of the Community Interpreter
Discuss how the role of the community interpreter supports communicative autonomy.

OBJECTIVE 5.2

Interpreting and Mediation
Discuss the complex relationship between interpreting and mediation.

OBJECTIVE 5.3

Advocacy and the Community Interpreter
Define advocacy and use a decision-making protocol to determine whether and how to advocate as a community interpreter.

OBJECTIVE 5.4

Standards of Practice
Identify general best practices for interpreters that support the Ethics and Standards document provided in this textbook.

OBJECTIVE 5.5

Self Care and Personal Wellness
Identify work-related risks for community interpreters and develop a wellness-and-safety plan.

OBJECTIVE 5.6

Professional Development
Create a professional development plan that supports high standards for community interpreting.

Learning Objective 5.1

After completing this section and its corresponding exercises, the learner will be able to:

- Discuss how the role of the community interpreter supports communicative autonomy.

 Learning Activity 5.1(a): The Interpreter's Role

Instructions

- In small groups, tell each other in your own words what you think "communicative autonomy" means. Do *not* look up the definition for this concept in the textbook.
- Next, compare your group's definition with the definition below, at the end of this activity. What is the same about it and your definition? What is different?
- Your instructor will now give your group a set of cards. Each card has written on it a common activity of community interpreters.
- Put them on the floor in order of *least* intrusive to *most* intrusive based on the degree to which the interpreter is potentially interfering with communicative autonomy.
- For example, *Restrict your activities to interpreting* is the least intrusive of all interpreter activities so it would go FIRST. However, *Advocate for the service user* is potentially quite intrusive so it would go near the end or perhaps at the end, as your group decides.
- You will also have one green card and one red card. In a separate activity, if time permits group those cards that refer to activities that appear *appropriate and permissible* for community interpreters under the green card; then group those activities that appear *inappropriate* under the red card.
- Afterward, discuss with your instructor to determine which activities may be appropriate in your specialization (e.g., medical vs. social services interpreting) and/or in your geographic area of practice.
- Finally, answer the following questions after reading Section 5.1 (pp. 362-370) of *The Community Interpreter®: An International Textbook.*

1. What is meant by the "role" of the community interpreter and why does it matter?

_____

_____

_____

_____

_____

_____

2. Why can't interpreters just make their own decisions to "help out" a service user instead of following strict ethics, standards and protocols?

_____

_____

_____

_____

3. In this section of the textbook (on p. 368), having community interpreters adhere to a common set of professional practices rather than deviating from those practices "as needed" is compared to having a regularly scheduled public transportation system. Why was this analogy used? Do you agree with it? Why or why not?

_____

_____

_____

_____

Card items

Here is a list of the items on each card for this activity, in random order. If your instructor does not give you cards with these items, you can put them in order by inserting a number beside each one, going from *least* intrusive practice to *most* intrusive practice in terms of their potential interference with communicative autonomy.

1. Request clarification of anything you don't understand or can't interpret.
2. Request clarification of anything important that the patient or client doesn't seem to understand.
3. Advocate for the patient/client.
4. Restrict your activities to interpreting. Do not intervene.
5. Intervene to point out a cultural misunderstanding (e.g., *The interpreter suggests you ask the patient about a cultural belief called* susto).
6. Help the patient/client after the session (e.g., by explaining what the provider said).
7. Intervene to explain a cultural issue that caused a misunderstanding (e.g., explain a ritual or health remedy).
8. Request clarification of anything important that the patient doesn't seem to understand *if and only if* the consequences of *not* intervening could be serious.

Definition of communicative autonomy

The capacity of each party in an encounter to be responsible for and in control of his or her own communication.

 Learning Activity 5.1(b): "Role" Plays

Instructions

- In role play triads, act out any or all of the three of the following role plays as you have other role plays in this workbook.
- **Note** that each role play includes a decision (or more than one decision) that the interpreter will have to make—a decision affected by how the interpreter understands his or her role.
- Let one person play the interpreter for each role play.
- Improvise an appropriate ending for each role play based on any decisions made by the interpreter in response to the situations that each role play addresses.
- If time permits, your instructor may ask you to spend a few minutes after each role play discussing how the interpreter handled these situations and whether you all (including the person who played the interpreter) agree on the action taken or whether you think another action or decision might be preferable.
- Please remember, as you discuss the role plays, that in real life each situation is unique and there is no "one right answer" for such situations.

Role play A: Baby gender confusion (English-Spanish)

Note: For this role-play, please assume that the pediatrician is not using an electronic medical record but a printed growth chart; blue is for boys and pink is for girls. In addition, "Xóchitl" is a common feminine name in Mexico, and this baby is dressed in pink.

First-year pediatric resident:	Mrs. Quintana, I want to talk to you about your child…how do you pronounce his name?		
Patient:		Es Xóchitl ("sought-chil").	It's Xóchitl ("sought-chil").
First-year pediatric resident:	I want to talk to you about him. He is very small for his age and gender. I plotted his growth on the growth chart (holding a blue growth chart) and he is not actually growing appropriately. So I have a few questions.		
Patient:		Sí, doctora, pero nunca me habían dicho que había un problema con su tamaño o crecimiento. Todo estaba normal, eso fue lo que me dijeron la última vez que estuve aquí.	Yes, doctor, but I have never been told that there is a problem with her size or growth. The last time I was here, I was told that everything was normal.
First-year pediatric resident:	No, I see it right here on the growth chart (holding the blue growth chart). I would expect him to be much bigger now. Look, you can see that he is well below his curve and that concerns me. How are you feeding him?		
Patient:		Le doy pecho y fórmula, nada más, porque eso me lo dijeron aquí. Que no le de agua, ni papilla, nada.	I breastfeed and I give her formula, because that's what I was told to do: no water, no baby food, nothing else.
First-year pediatric resident:	OK, how often?		

Patient:		Pues…cada hora y media o dos horas le doy pecho por 15 minutos y si todavía tiene hambre, le doy fórmula.	Well, I breastfeed for 15 minutes every hour-and-a half or two hours, and if she's still hungry, then I give her formula.
First-year pediatric resident:	So about 10 times a day? That sounds about right, but is he getting enough milk?		
Patient:		Sí, yo creo que sí. Crié a mis tres hijos de la misma manera y ninguno ha tenido ningún problema. Mi hijo, el más grandecito, estaba un poco pequeño, pero ahora es un gigante. A las dos nenas, la bebé y su hermana, yo las veo normales.	Yes, I think she does. I raised my three children in the same way, and none of them had a problem. My son, the oldest, was a little small, but now he is a giant. And, my two girls, my middle daughter, and the baby, they seem fine to me.
First-year pediatric resident:	Does he throw up or spit up?		
Patient:		No, a veces regresa la comida o, si tiene mucha tos, luego vomita, pero eso le pasa muy pocas veces.	No, sometimes, she spits up or if she has a bad cough, then she vomits, but that rarely happens.
First-year pediatric resident:	Well something is just not right. He is way too small for a boy. The growth chart shows me that (holding the blue growth chart). I think we should get some blood tests. There are some hormones I want to check. Let me talk to my attendant and I will be right back.		

Role play B: The patient can't read (English-Spanish)

Note: This role play is different! *Allow the interpreter to read from the first part of script just like the provider and the patient in the first part* (a pre-brief or pre-encounter with the provider). But then when the role play says to take the workbook away from the interpreter, do so—and after that the interpreter, as usual, will play the interpreter (and interpret) *without* a script.

Part 1: Interpreter reads from script during the pre-brief with the provider.

Healthcare provider:	(to the interpreter) Hi, you are one of the interpreters, right? Can you help me with this patient? Here is the story: I have had to label her as "non-compliant." She didn't take very good care of her diabetes during her pregnancy, and the baby was born pretty big, but thank God, nothing worse happened.		
Interpreter:		Sure, I'm free and I can help you.	
Healthcare provider:	I have given this patient SO MUCH information so far, I don't understand why she has had such a hard time following it. We have a great service, you know, that provides really good, really thorough patient-aid materials. Someone from your department told me that the Spanish version is very good, that the translations are really good. So I understand—oh, here we are, room 7. Before we go in, I am trying to do her post-partum screening. She has her seven-year-old daughter and her baby with her.		
Interpreter:		OK, well let's see what's up. When we go in give me a second to introduce myself.	

Now make sure the interpreter puts his or her workbook down and continues the rest of the role play by interpreting <u>without a script</u>.

Healthcare provider:	Mrs. Ramirez, I brought an interpreter with me this time because I want to ask you a few things that I think are very important.		
Patient:		OK, doctora.	OK, doctor.
Healthcare provider:	All during your pregnancy, I gave you plenty of information and for some reason you didn't follow a lot of it. It made it hard for us to care for you.		
Patient:		Pues, doctora, hice mi mejor esfuerzo. Vine a todas mis citas e hice todo lo posible, pero a veces no entendía lo que se esperaba de mí.	Well, doctor, I did the best that I could. I came to all my appointments. I was here and involved at all my visits. But sometimes I didn't understand what was expected of me.
Healthcare provider:	But you should have said something. I always made it a point to give you plenty of information to take home and read. We have a good service that provides that information to patients, and it's in Spanish as well. I am told that it is well translated.		
Patient:		Si, doctora, gracias por darme las cosas en español. Se lo agradezco. No quería causar una molestia, eso es todo.	Yes, doctor—thank you for giving me the info in Spanish. I appreciate that. I didn't want to be a pain, that was all.

Healthcare provider:	But, what I don't understand is why it was so difficult. We were never able to get your sugar or your diet under control. The diet book we use usually works really well, and I know I gave you a few copies. Yes, I Can Eat That! is a great book for diabetes in pregnancy. I think it was a best-seller.		
Patient:		Le vuelvo a repetir-hice mi mejor esfuerzo. A veces, se presentan complicaciones en la vida y bajo esas circunstancias, uno sólo puede hacer su mejor esfuerzo y eso es todo (voice cracking a little, and eyes tearing up slightly).	I'll say it again. I did my best. Sometimes there are things that come up and make your life more difficult. All in all —you just have to do your best and that's it. (voice cracking a little, and eyes tearing up slightly).
Healthcare provider:	Never mind, what's done is done. The baby is a little big, but at least there are no other problems. So today we're here to check your incision and see how you're feeling after giving birth. How are you?		
Patient:		Más o menos.	So-so.
Healthcare provider:	At these visits, we usually check for any signs of post-partum depression, which is why I gave you the questionnaire to fill out. Since we had so many issues with the forms before, I'd like you to fill them out now while I type your info in your chart. I'll stay right here. Is that all right?		

Patient:		Uh…¿sí? (patient gets a little uncomfortable and motions for her daughter to come and stand next to her).	Uh …yes? (patient seems a little uncomfortable and motions for her daughter to come and stand next to her).
Healthcare provider:	(to the interpreter) Would you mind staying while she does this? I think it would be better; I will score it right here and then we can talk. Can you, please?		
Interpreter:		Sure. (the patient is staring at questionnaire and, very furtively, showing it to her daughter; her daughter shrugs her shoulders; they are mumbling between themselves and it is obvious that mom is getting more and more uncomfortable. As the interpreter you want to respect their privacy but you notice that the questionnaire that mom is holding, the one that she has been looking at for a good few minutes now, is upside down).	Sure. (The patient is staring at questionnaire and, very furtively, showing it to her daughter; her daughter shrugs her shoulders; they are mumbling between themselves and it is obvious that Mom is getting more and more uncomfortable. As the interpreter you want to respect their privacy but you notice that the questionnaire that Mom is holding, the one that she has been looking at for a good few minutes now, is upside down).

Now improvise a conclusion for this role play based on the response of the interpreter.

Role play C: The neurologist (English-Spanish)

Neurology fellow:	Good afternoon sir, I am Dr. Patel and I am a neurology fellow. I work with Dr. Chandavarkar, who will come in after we speak.		
Patient		(nods with mobile phone in hand, looking at it).	(nods with mobile phone in hand, looking at it).
Neurology fellow:	I need to confirm your information: You are Wendys Taveras, is that right? Date of birth is March 11, 1992.		
Patient:		Sí, lo que pasa es que nací en el 91, pero mi papá no me reconoció, sino hasta el 92. Luego se equivocaron en el Registro Civil y pusieron 92 en el acta de nacimiento. Tengo 24, no 23.	Yeah, what happened is that I was born in '91 but my dad didn't accept I was his until '92, and then when they went to get my birth certificate, they made a mistake and put '92. I'm 24, not 23.
Neurology fellow:	OK. We have 3/11/92; maybe you could try to change that up front. Who is this with you? (looking at interpreter)		
Patient:		Dice que es el intérprete y que va a traducir lo que usted diga…. (to the interpreter)…explícale lo que me acabas de decir a mí.	He says he's the interpreter…(to the interpreter)…Explain to him what you just told me.
Neurology fellow:	(to the interpreter) I thought you were a family member or a friend. I think I will be fine without you, maybe you could just sit there and if I need you, I'll let you know. All right?		

WAIT TO SEE WHAT THE INTERPRETER DOES, THEN CONTINUE

Patient:		Ya, vámonos concho, yo tengo que hacer.	C'mon, let's go, darn, I have things to do.
Neurology fellow:	Mr. Taveras, you are epileptic. You are here today as a follow up. We see you every six months, correct?		
Patient:		Sí. (looking at phone)	Yeah. (looking at phone)
Neurology fellow:	You take carbamazepine to control your seizures, right? Carbamazepine, that is the generic name; the brand name is Tegretol. You might know it by the brand name.		
Patient:		Sí, tomo mi pastillita cada mañana, sin falta.	Yeah, I take a pill every morning, for sure.
Neurology fellow:	Have you had any side effects, like blurred vision, diarrhea, continual headaches or loss of appetite?		
Patient:		No, todo perfecto.	No. Everything is good.
Neurology fellow:	How about trembling or stiffness in your muscles, stiffness in your limbs? Any trouble sleeping, concentrating or walking?		
Patient:		Tampoco.	uh-uh.
Neurology fellow:	How about dizziness, lightheadedness, nausea or vomiting?		
Patient:		No, tampoco.	Nope.
Neurology fellow:	When was the last time you had a seizure?		

Patient:		(patient's mobile phone rings, a loud merengue song, patient speaks to doctor in limited english) 'scewme, one minute, no problem (talks into mobile phone) Ahlow? 'ahlow'	(patient's mobile phone rings, a loud merengue song, patient speaks to doctor in limited English) Scewme, one minute, no problem. (talks into mobile phone) Ahlow? 'ahlow'
Neurology fellow:	(shrugs shoulders, frustrated)		
Patient:		(patient on the mobile phone) 'Deshawn?…….. my howse, five minute, my howse, five minute" (hands mobile phone to interpreter) explícale que estaré allí en media hora y que debiera tener el cheque listo para la máquina	(patient on the mobile phone) Deshawn…my howse, five minute, my howse, five minute. (hands mobile phone to interpreter) Tell him I'll be there in half an hour and he better have the check ready for the motor.

WAIT TO SEE WHAT THE INTERPRETER DOES, THEN CONTINUE

Neurology fellow:	Mr. Taveras, please, this is serious and we need to finish. When was the last time you had a seizure?		
Patient:		Ni me acuerdo, hace mucho ya.	I don't even remember, it's been a while.
Neurology fellow:	What does that mean? Like a year, two years, five years, what?		
Patient:		Me dio uno hace dos años, creo, pero fue leve, no me desmayé ni nada (phone rings) 'dígame… ya sé—dile que espere, ya voy'. Sí, como hace tres años.	I had one about two years ago, but it was nothing, I didn't even pass out. (phone rings) 'Hello…I know—tell him to wait, I am coming.' Yeah, about three years ago.
Neurology fellow:	(very frustrated) OK, I am going to refill your medicine for you, just wait here. To what pharmacy do you go?		

Patient:		La que está abierta las 24 horas…allí al lado de donde lavan los carros…	The one that is open 24 hours, next to where they wash the cars…
Neurology fellow:	Where is that? It says here Town Pharmacy. I will refill your medicine and send the prescription there. You can pick it up there later today. No changes; keep taking your medicine and come back in six months.		
Patient:		(mobile phone rings)	(mobile phone rings)

Learning Objective 5.2

After completing this section and its corresponding exercises, the learner will be able to:
- Discuss the complex relationship between interpreting and mediation.

 Learning Activity 5.2: The Meaning of Mediation

Instructions (Part A)

- Read Section 5.2 (pp. 371-379) of *The Community Interpreter®: An International Textbook*.
- In pairs or small groups, read the list of mediation examples below.
- Decide together whether each of the acts in the left hand column properly belongs to the role of the community interpreter (because it involves strategic mediation that is non-intrusive and focused on communicative autonomy) or whether it does not.
- As you do so, remember that other professions, including patient advocates or guides, professional intercultural mediators and health promoters, might be permitted to engage in forms of mediation that would be inappropriate for community interpreters.
- If time permits, discuss your answers with your class members to see if everyone agrees.

Strategic Mediation and the Interpreter's Role

For each statement, depending on whether you find the type of mediation addressed *appropriate* for community interpreters, put a checkmark in the YES, NO or MAYBE column.

	YES	NO	MAYBE
1. Ask the service user/patient to state the meaning of an idiom or regional expression he or she just used.			
2. Offer the service user/patient a ride home after the appointment.			
3. Ask the service/healthcare provider to re-explain a procedure in a different way to ensure it is clearly conveyed to the service user/patient.			
4. Agree to accompany the service user/patient to the next appointment.			
5. Explain to the patient how the healthcare system in that country works, or to a parent how the school system there works.			
6. Ask a provider to explain a basic concept (such as a consent form, financial qualification process or school progress report) to a service user/patient.			
7. Request a clarification of a term *not* because you do not understand it but because you are concerned that the service user/patient doesn't understand it.			
8. Refer a service user/patient who is experiencing domestic or gender-based violence to a local shelter for victims of abuse.			
9. Invite a refugee for whom you interpreted and who is going hungry to a dinner in your home.			
10. Explain to a service/healthcare provider how men and women interact in the service user/patient's culture.			
11. Mediate in a dispute between a divorcing husband and wife.			
12. Suggest to an upset service user/patient who is cursing that s/he calm down in order not to risk losing the service.			

Instructions, Part B

- Now revisit the list above.
- Decide, for each item, if this action would be appropriate (yes, no or maybe) for an *intercultural or cultural mediator* (or a patient guide/patient navigator if you are a medical interpreter).

Learning Activity 5.3

After completing this section and its corresponding exercises, the learner will be able to:

- Define advocacy and use a decision-making protocol to determine whether and how to advocate as a community interpreter.

 Learning Activity 5.3(a): Maria's Mom

Instructions

- In pairs or small groups, read Story A below—medical interpreters, select Story B—then answer the question following it and discuss your answer with your peers.
- Next, consider the definition of advocacy provided in *The Community Interpreter®: An International Textbook*, which is: **Taking action or speaking up on behalf of a service user or patient whose safety, health, well-being or human dignity is at risk, with the purpose of preventing such harm.**
- Now discuss this broader question: Would you advocate in a situation like the one in this story? Why or why not?

Story A: Maria's mom

> Maria had never been a successful student, but it was her behavior at school—which was becoming more and more problematic—that had caused her to be suspended from class for three days. Now she faced a disciplinary hearing and might be expelled.
>
> Maria, her mother and the principal of her high school all gathered to discuss the situation. The interpreter could not believe what she heard when the principal asked Maria: "Do you want to become a no-one like your mum? Or do you want to be able to get a real job and go somewhere in life? If you want a job and a good life, you'd better try hard. We're here to help, but you have to do your part."

What would you do if you were the interpreter in the session with Maria's principal? Would you:

a. Avoid interpreting the offensive reference to the mom (simply omit it).
b. Apply the 5 steps of strategic mediation to tell the principal that his comments are racist.
c. Tell the mother that the principal was being racist, but only once the session is over.
d. None of the above: interpret everything that is said and avoid any further involvement.

Story B: Maria's mom and the doctor

Maria's mother took her to the doctor for her first appointment with a gynecologist when Maria was 15. When the doctor asked if she had engaged in sexual activity or not, Maria blushed and said no, she hadn't. The doctor, after a physical examination, determined that, in fact, Maria had engaged in sexual activity and he told her, in front of her mother, "Do you want to become a no one like your mom, pregnant at 15 and with no future? And maybe get a sexually transmitted infection like HIV? Or do you want to finish high school, go to university and get somewhere in life? Because if that's what you want, you'd better buckle down and stop having sex and lying about it, or at least take some preventive measures."

What would you do if you were the interpreter in the appointment with Maria's doctor? Would you:

a. Avoid interpreting the offensive reference about the mom (simply omit it)?
b. Apply the five steps of the Strategic Mediation Model to tell the doctor that his/her comments are racist or bigoted?
c. Tell the mother, after the appointment, that the doctor was a bigot?
d. Simply interpret everything said and avoid any further involvement?

 Learning Activity 5.3(b): Follow the Road Map

Instructions

- Read Section 5.3 (pp. 380-393) of *The Community Interpreter®: An International Textbook*
- In pairs or small groups, choose at least two of the situations below. Medical interpreters should select two of the three healthcare scenarios: B, D or E.
- Apply the advocacy roadmap to decide if, and how, you would advocate in each of the situations you choose.
- If time permits, you can discuss other scenarios from the list.

Scenarios

A. The parents have just met with a teacher at the school and you are quite sure they believe their child, who has a learning disability, is about to enter a program for gifted and talented students. The parents do not understand that their child is, in fact, about to receive the services of a reading specialist. Your attempts at strategic mediation during the session failed. Yet the teacher seems quite unaware of any confusion.

B. The doctor has left. The patient begs you to explain what the doctor said about the preoperative instructions. You can't get another healthcare provider to speak to the patient and you must leave for another interpreting assignment.

C. The refugee you interpreted for has just been denied food assistance and other benefits because the time for such benefits has expired. Right after the session, a community leader who you respect comes up to you and insists that you, the interpreter, *must help* this refugee find housing assistance and food. The leader says it is your duty to help others less fortunate. You are aware that the refugee's family is, indeed, about to go hungry and might also be evicted from their temporary housing.

D. The asylum seeker was tortured in a prison with lights. You have interpreted for this person in multiple types of appointments so you know that history. Now at an eye appointment, an optometrist is flashing lights at the asylum seeker, who falls into a trance dissociative state. The optometrist is upset and confused.

E. The hospital patient is dying. A construction worker is injured in the workplace; he comes from a culture where he probably would not want a hospital chaplain to visit him (although you are not completely sure of this). But when the chaplain comes and the patient shuts down completely, you have nothing to interpret. The patient is not articulate and has very little education. No family members are present. The chaplain has no understanding of the patient's indigenous beliefs or what to do to help the patient.

 Learning Activity 5.3(c): Consider the Consequences: Advocacy Role Plays

Instructions

- In role play triads, act out one of the two Maria stories above and see what the interpreter does.
- Improvise a conclusion based on the interpreter's decision.
- Now change the scenario and instead have the principal or doctor say that Maria will be expelled from the school (story A), which means she will not graduate on time, or denied services at that clinic (story B), even though she has a serious prenatal condition that requires medical attention.
- The interpreter should follow the advocacy roadmap.
- If you wish, and the interpreter wants to report something after the appointment, improvise a scenario that allows the interpreter to do so.
- Note that the role play perhaps ends with a consequence. Discuss what happened and if you all agree with the interpreter's course of action.
- Please remember, as you discuss the role plays after acting them out, that in real life each situation is unique *and there is no "one right answer" for some of the situations that you will encounter as a community interpreter.*

Learning Objective 5.4

After completing this section and its corresponding exercises, the learner will be able to:

- Identify general best practices for interpreters that support the Ethics and Standards document provided in this textbook.

 Learning Activity 5.4(a): Always, Sometimes, Rarely

Instructions (Part A)

- Your instructor will provide, where available, the code of ethics or conduct, or standards of practice or a professional guidelines document, that most closely applies to you wherever you practice. (Such a document could be created by, for example, a professional association or group; a federal or state/provincial/municipal court; an interpreting service provider; a school system; or a healthcare organization.) For example, in the United States that document would be the *National Code of Ethics for Interpreters in Health Care* published in 2004 by the National Council on Interpreting in Health Care.
- Compare that document with the *Ethics and Standards* on pp. 1-30 of *The Community Interpreter®: An International Textbook.*
- Write in the columns below at least three things you find that are the *same* in each document and at least three things that are *different*.
- Then proceed to Part B of this exercise.

What is the same?

_____

_____

_____

_____

_____

What is different?

_____

_____

_____

_____

_____

Instructions (Part B)

- Use the document given to you by your instructor or the *Ethics and Standards* document from the textbook, depending on the decision of your instructor.
- In pairs or small groups, take each standard in the document and write its number down in one of the three columns below.
- Make that decision based on answering the following question for each standard: *Before you read the textbook, did you apply Standard X always (or almost always); sometimes; or rarely.*
- You can discuss your answers with your partner(s) but write only *your own* answers in the columns below.
- Then proceed to Part C of this exercise.

I used to **always** apply this standard…	**Sometimes** I applied this standard(s) …	I used to **rarely** apply this standard…

Instructions (Part C)

- Use the document given to you by your instructor or the *Ethics and Standards* document from the textbook, depending on the decision of your instructor.
- Answer the question below.

In the blank lines provided, write down which standard of practice (by number, if possible, depending on the document used) that you and your group finds the most:

1. *Surprising.*
2. *Difficult to implement in real life.*
3. *Helpful.*

Surprising: _____

Difficult: _____

Helpful: _____

 Learning Activity 5.4(b): Traffic Lights: Applying Standards

Instructions

- Read the list below. It is made up of common interpreting practices, some of them professional and some of them unprofessional for community/medical interpreters.
- In pairs or small groups, decide whether the practice is something you should always (or almost always) do; sometimes or often do; or never/rarely do.
- If the practice is something you should always (or almost always) do, write G for green in the blank line following the statement. If the practice is something you would often or sometimes do, write Y for yellow (think—*Caution! Slow down!*). If it is something you should rarely if ever do, write R for red.
- If time permits, your instructor will give each of you, or perhaps your group, a red, green and yellow circle.
- The whole group will go through the statements one at a time. Hold up the color you find appropriate for that statement—and see if everyone in the class agrees!

Common interpreting practices

Which practices are almost always acceptable (green light)?
Almost never acceptable (red light)?
Sometimes acceptable (yellow light ?)

1. Interpret everything stated by all parties.
2. If the service user asks your opinion, offer it.
3. If the provider forgets certain information that is important, add it in yourself.
4. Maintain strict confidentiality, always.
5. To avoid causing cultural offense, accept a grateful service user's small gift of money even if you are paid by an organization.
6. Ask parties to address each other and not the interpreter.
7. Allow your personal beliefs to influence your decisions as an interpreter.
8. Interpret body language, gestures and facial expressions.
9. Simplify what a provider says when s/he uses language that the service user doesn't seem to understand.
10. Plan to arrive exactly on time for the session.
11. Discuss an interpreted session with a colleague, including details.
12. Use direct speech (first person) to interpret.
13. Give the service provider a ride to the next appointment.
14. Interpret for friends or members of your family at the hospital.
15. Interpret in a flat, monotone voice without emotion.
16. Convey the intent of the message, including its spirit and expressivity.
17. Share information about a public event where you interpreted (e.g., a school event, a health education seminar or an immigration services public presentation).
18. Break confidentiality in cases of imminent danger (a very short-term risk of *homicide* or *suicide*).
19. Break confidentiality if required by law.
20. Call yourself "certified" if you have a certificate for taking a training or workshop.
21. Use dictionaries during the assignment (print or electronic).
22. Interpret "fillers" (small noises like *er, uh, umm,* etc.) that do not hold content-based meaning but instead convey the idea the speaker is thinking what to say next.
23. Instead of sight translating a complex, long legal form, ask the provider to explain it and interpret the explanation.
24. Withdraw if you become emotionally affected or distressed.
25. Support the service user/patient after the session if an unfair situation arises.
26. Request a break when you notice your accuracy is impaired by your tiredness.
27. Mediate to explain a cultural tradition.
28. Stay in the room with the service user/patient when the service provider steps out for a moment.
29. If the service provider asks you to sight translate a short document without the service provider present, and the document is easy, do so.
30. Interpret offensive statements (from any party) completely and accurately.
31. Assist service users with forms (by explaining the questions and writing down the answers while the provider does something else).
32. Assist service users with forms (by sight translating the questions and writing down the answers while the service provider remains to answer questions).
33. Assist service users with forms (by sight translating the questions and letting the service provider or user write down the answers).
34. Refer service users who need assistance to the appropriate social services.

Learning Activity 5.4(c): The Standards of Practice Role Play Game

Instructions

- Use the document given to you by your instructor or the *Ethics and Standards* document from the textbook, depending on the decision of your instructor.
- In groups of three, select one standard and create a skit or little role play to show that standard being violated. *Medical interpreters should select a healthcare setting for their role play.*
- Each group will take turns (time permitting) acting out the role play in front of the class.
- The class will then guess which standard your group selected. Do not give the answer until someone in the class guesses correctly.

Learning Objective 5.5

After completing this section and its corresponding exercises, the learner will be able to:
- Identify work-related risks for community interpreters and develop a wellness- and-safety plan.

 Learning Activity 5.5(a): Delivering Rough News: A Role Play

Instructions

- In role play triads, act out the following role play as you have other role plays in this workbook.
- Afterward, let the person who plays the interpreter decide how it felt to be the interpreter for that role play.
- Next, if time permits, your instructor may have someone in the group tell a true-life story about a time he or she interpreted for an assignment that was distressing the interpreter.
- After the role play and/or story, discuss *what actions the interpreter could take to feel better following the assignment.* The instructor may note these suggestions down on a marker board, easel or computer display.
- The interpreter will remain silent until the group has finished making suggestions, and then will state which ones might have helped him or her feel better after the distressing assignment.

Role play: Delivering rough news[40]

Doctor:	Mr. Abad, after carefully reviewing all the tests done on your son, we are sure that your son has <u>retinoblastoma.</u>		
Parent:		¿Puede explicarme eso? ¿Qué es eso?	Can you explain this to me? What is it?
Doctor:	Retinoblastoma is a disease of the eye.		
Parent:		Qué tipo de enfermedad?	What type of disease?
Doctor:	Cells have multiplied quickly in your son's eye, forming a tumor in the retina.		
Parent:		¿¡Un tumor?! Estoy seguro que usted puede operar el tumor y liberarlo de ese tumor, ¿verdad?	A tumor?! But I'm sure you can operate on the tumor and get it out, right?
Doctor:	Well it is not that easy, the tumor has filled his eyeball		
Parent:		¿Qué está tratando de decirme? ¿No puede operarle el ojo?	What are you trying to tell me? You can't operate on his eye?
Doctor:	There are some treatments available.		
Parent:		Qué bueno, ¿cuándo empezamos?	Great, when do we start?

[40]Adapted from Bancroft and Rubio-Fitzpatrick (2011), *The Community Interpreter: A Comprehensive Training Manual*, 5th ed. Columbia, MD: Culture & Language Press, pp. 110-112.

Doctor:	Before I can discuss treatment, I must explain other things. Your son will be losing his sight and will become blind. We do not know how long this will take but we know he will not be able to see. I want you to understand this.		
Parent:		¡NO! ¡¡ESTO NO PUEDE SUCEDER!! ¡¡¡NO!!!	NO!!! THIS CAN'T BE HAPPENING!! NO!!!
Doctor:	I know… It's a lot to take in…		
Parent:		A el le fascina leer y está aprendiendo a manejar. ¡El quiere ir a la escuela y quiere ir a la universidad! El es un alumno nuevo y tiene muchas ilusiones con su futuro.	He loves to read and he's learning how to drive. He wants to go to school and he wants to go to college! He's a new student and he has a lot of dreams about his future.
Doctor:	We'll have to refer him to other specialists and make sure he receives special services in school since he is going to go blind. I am going to schedule him for an immediate follow up appointment with Dr. Good so he can discuss treatment with you. I recommend you set up an appointment with Dr. Good as soon as possible.		

Doctor Good:	Mr. Abad, I received your son's medical file and I have reviewed it carefully. I am very sorry that your son has this disease.		
Parent:		¿Es un tumor en su ojo pero usted es el especialista, usted puede operarlo y sacarle esa cosa, cierto?	It's a tumor in his eye but you're the specialist, you can operate on him and get this thing out for sure, right?
Doctor:	Yes, we can operate but that is not going to resolve the problem since your son will lose his vision. It's completely taken over by these tumors. More in the right eye than in the left eye.		
Parent:		¿Pero va a poder ver algo en su ojo derecho, cierto?	But he'll be able to see with his right eye, right?
Doctor:	Maybe for a little while but I do not know how much or for how long.		
Parent:		¿Por qué? ¿Qué la cirugía no va a resolver el problema? POR FAVOR, POR FAVOR, SE LO RUEGO, ¡¡¡AYUDE A MI HIJO!!!	Why? Isn't surgery going to take care of the problem? PLEASE, PLEASE, I'M BEGGING YOU, HELP MY CHILD!!!

Instructions

- Read Section 5.5 (pp. 415-431) of *The Community Interpreter®: An International Textbook*, or listen to your instructor discuss the content with you.
- Look at the diagrams below, taken from pp. 416 and 426 of your textbook.
- For each of the six hazards on the left, identify at least one problem or symptom that you either have (a) already experienced as a community interpreter; or (b) imagine you could experience as a community interpreter. Write them down in the lines provided.
- For each of the six problems or symptoms, imagine a concrete self-care activity that might be helpful and write it down.
- Be sure to make your suggested activities SMART (specific, measurable, appropriate, realistic and time-bound).

_____

_____

_____

_____

_____

_____

_____

_____

_____

_____

_____

_____

_____

_____

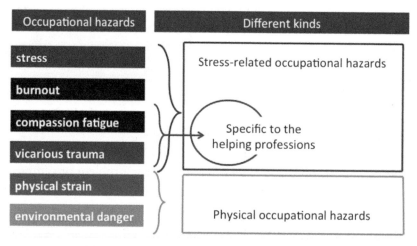

Table 5-L: Types and Kinds of Occupational Hazards

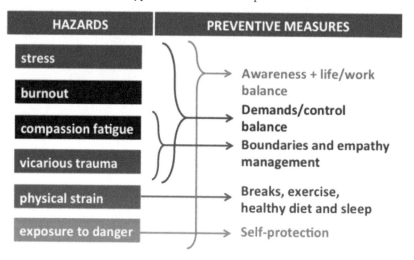

Table 5-M: Preventive Measures

 Learning Activity 5.5(c): Your Self-Care Plan

Instructions

- Write a self-care plan in two parts: long-term and short-term (before, during and after a difficult assignment).
- To help you, look up any available resources. One that is recommended for this exercise and that may be available to you is Chapter Two of *Breaking Silence: Interpreting for Victim Services*[41], which will be available online at no cost in 2016.
- Part One of your self-care plan should focus on long-term wellness activities that support four well-established aspects of wellness: adequate sleep; exercise and activity; eating well; and relaxation.
- Part Two of your self-care plan should focus on activities you can engage in before, during and after assignments that are, or could be, distressing for you.
- Bring your self-care plan to class and be prepared to give examples from it.

---

[41]Bancroft, M.A., Allen, K., Feuerle, L and Green, C. in press. *Breaking Silence: Interpreting for Victim Services.* Washington, DC: Ayuda.

Learning Objective 5.6

After completing this section and its corresponding exercises, the learner will be able to:

- Create a professional development plan that supports high professional standard for community interpreting.

 Learning Activity 5.6(a): Elements of a Plan for Professional Development

Instructions

- Read Section 5.6 (pp. 432-442) of *The Community Interpreter®: An International Textbook.*
- Look at the sample professional development checklist on p. 437, reproduced to the right.
- Write down, in the blank lines provided, any professional development activities for community interpreters that you have engaged in.
- Next, write down professional development activities you would like to engage in for the first time, or more often, in the near future.
- Finally, write down first steps you would need to take. For example, in order join a listserv for interpreters in your area, you might need to join the professional association that sponsors it. To take a workshop on medical terminology, you might need to research local or online options available to you.

Professional development checklist

EVENTS

- ❏ Attend interpreter conferences, workshops or seminars.
- ❏ Sign up for online webinars.
- ❏ Take training course online or in person

PEER-SUPPORT ACTIVITIES

- ❏ Set up "study buddy" sessions.
- ❏ Join interpreter groups in social media.
- ❏ Subscribe to interpreter blogs and listservs.

PERSONAL TASKS

- ❏ Create specialized glossaries.
- ❏ Study the glossaries.
- ❏ Record myself and do a written self-assessment.
- ❏ Keep a journal of my professional evolution.
- ❏ Listen to the radio and read online newspapers in my different languages.

Professional activities I have engaged in

_____

_____

_____

_____

_____

Professional activities I want to engage in soon

_____

_____

_____

_____

_____

First steps I need to take to engage in those activities

_____

_____

_____

_____

_____

Learning Activity 5.6(b): My Top Three Goals

Instructions

- Decide on the *top three activities* you will engage in after leaving this training program to further your professional development.
- As with your self care plan, make your suggested activities SMART (specific, measurable, appropriate, realistic and time-bound).
- One activity should focus on your *linguistic skills* and language proficiency: maintaining both (or all) your working languages (such as taking higher education classes, listening to television programs in your weaker language or reading medical information about chronic diseases in both or all your working languages).
- One activity should focus on enhancing your *message transfer skills* (such as online courses, partner practice or self-study activities to help with memory, analysis, chunking, visualization or note-taking).
- One activity should focus on *professional identity and/or your specialization* (such as attending a professional association conference, taking a workshop on medical terminology, or subscribing to a medical or community interpreting listserv and participating).
- Write your three top-priority activities in the lines provided.

My top three goals for professional development

_____

_____

_____

_____

_____

_____

_____

_____

_____

_____

_____